The Open University

Practising Science Study Book

This publication forms part of an Open University course SXR103 *Practising science*. Details of this and other Open University courses can be obtained from the Student Registration and Enquiry Service, The Open University, PO Box 197, Milton Keynes MK7 6BJ, United Kingdom: tel. +44 (0)845 300 60 90, email general-enquiries@open.ac.uk

Alternatively, you may visit the Open University website at http://www.open.ac.uk where you can learn more about the wide range of courses and packs offered at all levels by The Open University.

To purchase a selection of Open University course materials visit http://www.ouw.co.uk, or contact Open University Worldwide, Walton Hall, Milton Keynes MK7 6AA, United Kingdom for a brochure. tel. +44 (0)1908 858793; fax +44 (0)1908 858787; email ouw-customer-services@open.ac.uk

The Open University
Walton Hall, Milton Keynes
MK7 6AA

First published 2001. Second edition 2003. Third edition 2007. Fourth edition 2008, Fifth edition 2010.

Edited and designed by The Open University.

Typeset by SR Nova Pvt Ltd, Bangalore, India.

Printed and bound in the United Kingdom by Halstan Printing Group, Amersham.

ISBN 978 1 8487 3276 6

5.1

The paper used in this publication contains pulp sourced from forests independently certified to the Forest Stewardship Council (FSC) principles and criteria. Chain of custody certification allows the pulp from these forests to be tracked to the end use (see www.fsc-uk.org).

Contents

Chapter 1
Introduction: the future of practical science

1.1   Science and scientists

Science is all about knowledge: what we know about the material world and the Universe in which our world is just a microscopic speck. The aim of scientists is to extend the frontiers of this knowledge so that we can understand more about the physical Universe and the life within it.

Scientists acquire knowledge by engaging in four fundamentally important and connected tasks. The first is *observation*: they observe the natural world and the space beyond it, and both describe and record what they see. Second, they *construct hypotheses* to explain what they see. Third, they do experiments where possible to *test their hypotheses*. Finally they *communicate their findings* to other scientists who will build on this work to extend knowledge still further, to technologists who will devise practical applications for scientific knowledge and to the general public to raise awareness of scientific discovery. The way in which science is communicated to interested parties is especially important because scientific knowledge is useless if no one else can understand it.

You may find that practising science in a laboratory or field setting is what you will enjoy most about this course. However, graduate scientists leaving universities must be able to demonstrate that they have gained the skills needed to engage effectively with *each* of the tasks described above. You will be introduced to these skills during the Residential School component of *Practising science* and you will engage with all of the tasks of the scientist as you work through the Residential School activities.

1.2   Introducing the *Practising Science Study Book*

You will need an understanding of some basic concepts of science and of practical techniques if you want to get the maximum benefit from the activities at the Residential School. The aim of this book is to provide this background. As well as studying the material, it is important that you *read through each of the activity workbooks before you attend the Residential School*, to become familiar with the work you will be asked to do. We don't expect you to spend a lot of time on this, or to understand everything in the workbooks. Some of it will make sense only as you carry out an activity. However, familiarity beforehand will allow you to progress more easily through the activities and to appreciate their outcomes more fully. You will find it helpful to re-read the summaries in the Course Guide to gain an overview of each activity before reading the associated workbook.

The following chapters introduce some of the concepts and practical techniques in Earth sciences, physics, biology and chemistry that underpin the various Residential School activities. They also give you practice in extracting information from a scientific article, a skill that will be developed as you learn how to communicate science to other people. Remember that there is a separate online *Glossary* containing definitions of the scientific terms introduced in this book, which are printed in bold, e.g. **atom**. You will also find a number of questions and activities in the text that you should complete. (Note: the answers to activities and questions can be found in sections at the end of this book.)

1.3 Doing science safely

It is important to carry out scientific experiments and field work in a manner that is safe for you and those working with you. For this reason all activities go through a 'risk assessment' process. During this process the associated **hazards** are identified, the associated **risk** is evaluated and safety measures stated. For example, a briefcase or bag left on a laboratory floor is hazardous because people working there may trip over it, perhaps hurting themselves or damaging equipment. The risk associated with this **event** (or **procedure**) may vary depending on whether the laboratory is crowded, what sort of work is being done and what equipment is being used. The type of safety measure that could be used to reduce the risks is to require that all bags are placed in lockers or on shelves away from the laboratory benches (this removes the hazard).

Terms such as hazard and risk in everyday language may seem interchangeable but within a health and safety context have very distinct definitions:

An event or procedure is the circumstance or action which may lead to a hazard.

A hazard is the potential to do harm.

Risk is the likelihood that a hazard will cause harm.

Please don't be concerned that laboratories and field locations are dangerous though! There are element of danger in most aspects of everyday life and people often apply safety measures instinctively or by using common sense.

Think of your everyday surroundings and identify a hazard. What sort of harm could this hazard cause? What safety measures would you take to minimise the risk of that harm?

Here are some examples:

Procedure or Event	Hazard	Measures taken to reduce risk
Boiling water	scald hazard	avoid contact between boiling water and skin
Busy road	collision hazard	be aware of other road users
Toxic household chemicals	poisoning hazard	take care not to ingest

You might have thought of other examples, but note that the hazard in itself does not cause harm. It is the combination of the hazard and inappropriate or careless actions that is harmful, which is why people take sensible precautions.

While you are at the Residential School, the following general rules will apply.

Safety and conduct in the laboratory

1   For your own protection:

you must wear a laboratory coat (properly fastened); to avoid contaminating other items, laboratory coats should not be worn outside the laboratory

you must wear safety glasses and gloves when instructed to do so

long hair must be tied back, so that it does not get caught in any apparatus

you must not wear open-toed shoes or sandals

you must not wear shorts or skirts that are above the knee

any existing cuts or grazes on your hands must be covered with waterproof plasters before starting any practical work.

2   You must not enter or remain in the laboratory unless a tutor is present.

3   You must follow the instructions in the workbook and must not alter any experimental procedure. You must not handle equipment, instruments or chemicals that are not part of the activity.

4   You should report immediately any mishaps, however minor, to a tutor.

5   You should treat all chemicals as potentially hazardous, and take care when handling chemicals and glassware. The gloves that are provided should be worn when handling chemicals.

6   Any chemical spilt or splashed on your skin or mouth should be washed off immediately with large quantities of water.

7   Any chemical spilt or splashed into your eyes should be washed off immediately with the laboratory eyewash provided. You should also tell a tutor.

8   Smoking, eating and drinking in the laboratory are forbidden.

9   Always wash your hands when leaving the laboratory and before eating.

10 To prevent trips and falls you should move about the laboratory and surrounding corridors carefully, and keep all passageways clear of bags, coats, etc.

11 If you need to leave the laboratory between 'official' breaks tell your tutor, who may be just about to brief the group on the next stage of the investigation.

Other safety measures that are appropriate to individual activities are given in the workbooks. Your tutors will discuss these with you as part of your introduction to each activity.

You should now carry out the online activity 'Doing Science Safely'. There is a link to this on the SXR103 course website.

1.4   What to do next

There is one final task before you move on to Chapter 2 of this book. The language of science depends heavily on numbers and symbols. You should check now that you are confident using symbols, such as chemical symbols and units of measurement. You can check this, and check that you have understood the material on doing science safely, by working through the online interactive self-assessment questions for Chapter 1. You can access these questions via the link on the SXR103 course website.

Chapter 2
Earth sciences: reading the rocks

This chapter is relevant to parts of Activity A 'Rocks and radioactivity' and Activity C 'Investigating the environment'.

2.1   Introduction

The Earth sciences concern every part of our planet – from the centre of the metallic core, 6400 km below your feet, through its solid and liquid regions (Figure 2.1), to the outer reaches of the atmosphere. However, at this point in the course you will concentrate on the outermost, rocky part of the solid Earth: the rocks of the Earth's crust that form the uppermost layer of the lithospheric plates. On the scale of a human lifetime, these rocks and the landscapes they are part of can seem static and immutable, at least in a country such as Britain where there are no active volcanoes, and earthquakes are infrequent and fairly small. None the less, coastal erosion and the biological degradation of rocks to form soils are reminders that geological processes are occurring 'in your own backyard' and that the Earth's surface is continuously being reshaped.

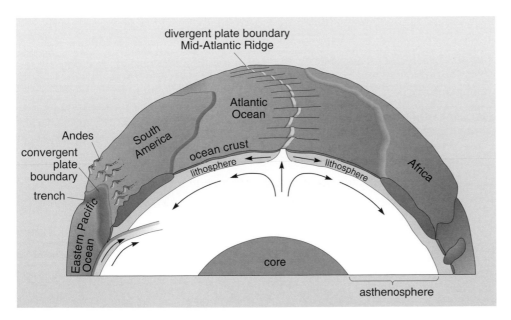

Figure 2.1   Schematic cross-section through the Earth, showing its concentrically layered internal structure and the interacting lithospheric plates on the surface.

Over hundreds of millions of years, the surface of the Earth is rearranged by the slow grinding of geological processes. In particular, the rigid outer layer of the Earth (around 100 km thick and called the lithosphere) is divided into about 12 plates, which change shape, size and position as their margins grow, destruct or collide (see Figure 2.1). So, although the processes can be very slow, given enough time the results include the generation and destruction of mountain ranges that stretch across continents, and the opening and closing of ocean basins. All of these geological processes leave their mark by forming new rocks. And those rocks – whether sandstone formed from sand in a desert, or volcanic lava flows – hold clues to the processes that formed them and, therefore, the conditions at the time of their formation. In some cases they contain information about past climatic conditions; some rocks contain fossils that reveal the history of life and the story of evolution. Rocks can provide a narrative of the Earth's history, but you need to learn how to read their tales.

At the Residential School you will experience the practical aspects of studying rocks and piecing together the evidence of how they formed. This will involve you in examining rocks exposed in the field (as part of Activity C 'Investigating the environment') and rock specimens in the laboratory (as part of Activity A 'Rocks and radioactivity: energy in the Earth'). Both types of investigation are important in geology – the study of rocks and the information that they hold about the history of Earth through its 4600 million year history.

In the practical work you will deduce how particular rocks were formed and the sequence of events in the geological history of a small part of Britain. As with many other areas of science, you will first gather data by making careful observations. Then those observations will be interpreted in a way that best explains them.

The aims of this chapter are to:

- demonstrate how many of the features shown by rocks are inherited from the processes that formed them
- introduce the skills of sketching features seen in rock exposures
- show how those features can be interpreted in a simple sequence of events through geological time.

2.2   Minerals and rocks

First, it is necessary to explain the meaning of the terms 'minerals' and 'rocks'.

2.2.1 Minerals

A **mineral** is a solid material, formed by natural processes, with a chemical composition that falls within certain narrow limits. Its constituent atoms are arranged in a regular, three-dimensional array or pattern and, because of this, minerals form crystals with characteristic shapes.

Although several thousand different minerals have been discovered, only a few are very common; for example, the mineral quartz, which forms many of the sand grains on a beach or in a desert. Because silicon and oxygen are the two most **abundant** elements in the Earth's crust, they are the main ingredients of the common minerals, which are called **silicate minerals**. They include **quartz**, whose chemical composition is silicon dioxide (formula SiO_2), and a range of others containing additional common chemical elements. A common mineral that is *not* a silicate is **calcite**; its chemical composition is calcium carbonate ($CaCO_3$). Whereas most minerals are identified on the basis of physical characteristics (density, hardness, colour, etc.), calcite can also be readily identified with a chemical test. Calcite reacts with dilute hydrochloric acid (HCl), liberating bubbles of carbon dioxide (CO_2) gas in a vigorous, fizzing froth. You will see this characteristic reaction in the work you do at the Residential School. The chemical reaction is written as:

$$CaCO_3(s) + H^+(aq) + Cl^-(aq) \longrightarrow Ca^{2+}(aq) + OH^-(aq) + Cl^-(aq) + CO_2(g) \qquad (2.1)$$

In words, this equation can be expressed as: solid calcium carbonate (calcite) plus hydrogen ions in the acid plus chloride ions in the acid gives calcium ions, hydroxide ions and chloride ions dissolved in solution plus carbon dioxide gas.

You will get more practice in reading and using chemical equations when you study chemistry in Chapter 5.

2.2.2 Rocks

Any naturally formed, solid assemblage of mineral grains can be described as a **rock**. The mineral grains may be fragments of crystals or intact crystals, and can range in size from a few micrometres (1 micrometre = 10^{-6} m or 0.000 001 m) to a few centimetres. A rock may consist of one type of mineral but, more usually, several minerals. Rocks can be classified according to how the grains are arranged, although the identity of the minerals present (for example, the rock **limestone** is made mostly of calcite), the proportions of particular minerals, and the dominant size of the mineral grains are also important. The shape of the grains in a rock, their size and the relationship between them (whether or not the grains interlock with each other to form a mosaic or are less neatly aligned) define the **texture** of a rock, and reflect the processes that formed it. A rock's texture has nothing to do with how the rock feels when you touch it. To 'read the rocks' and discover how any particular rock formed, you need to investigate its texture and work backwards to deduce the processes which produced that texture.

The mineral grains in most rocks are quite small so it is often best to use a hand lens, typically with a magnification power of ×10, to get a clearer view. If you already have a small hand lens, it is a good idea to practise using it before the Residential School. There are some notes on this in Box 2.1.

Box 2.1   Using a hand lens

The correct way to examine objects with a hand lens is shown in Figure 2.2a.

- Hold the hand lens 2–3 cm from your eye and bring the object up towards the lens until it is in focus.
- Make sure the surface of the object is well lit from the side.
- Keep the hand lens and the object parallel to each other and hold both steady.
- With rough surfaces you have to move the object back and forth to bring different parts into focus.
- If you use eye wear, such as glasses, experiment to see whether it is better to remove them when using a hand lens.
- If you have a visual impairment that prevents you using a hand lens you may find you can use another form of magnifier to examine rocks. Several will be available for use in Activity A at the Residential School.

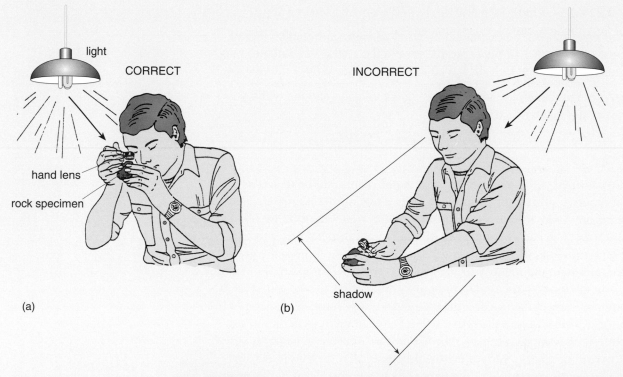

Figure 2.2   (a) Correct use of a hand lens. (b) Incorrect use of a hand lens.

Rocks are classified into three types, according to the three processes that form them.

1   **Igneous rocks**: these are formed from molten rock (**magma**) which solidifies when it cools, either deep underground or after a volcanic eruption at the surface.

2   **Sedimentary rocks**: these are formed when eroded particles of pre-existing rocks (in other words sediment, such as sand on a beach or mud

on the seabed) have been laid down in layers at the Earth's surface and turned into solid rock by being buried and compacted under more layers of sediment.

3   **Metamorphic rocks**: these are existing rocks that have 'changed form' by the action of high pressure or temperature causing new crystals to grow, for example after burial deep in the Earth.

Sections 2.3 to 2.5 describe in more detail how each of the three major rock types is formed, and how their modes of formation can be deduced from the textures and other features visible in the rocks themselves – 'reading the rocks'. These sections relate to your work during the first part of Activity A 'Rocks and radioactivity: energy in the Earth'. Some of this knowledge will also be used during Activity C 'Investigating the environment', where you will do some fieldwork observing the rocks and interpreting the geological history of an area near your Residential School. After pausing to recap your learning in Section 2.6, Section 2.7 introduces some of the practices of field geology. Section 2.8 is an overview of how the geological processes that form new rocks act on pre-existing rocks in a cycle of destruction, formation and transformation called the rock cycle. Section 2.9 addresses an ongoing geological process – sea-level change – and Section 2.10 refers you to the workbook for Activity C 'Investigating the environment'. There is a summary of the chapter in Section 2.11.

2.3   The formation of igneous rocks

Igneous rocks are defined as having solidified from a molten state, either inside the Earth or at the surface in volcanoes.

2.3.1   Igneous rocks in the landscape

The rocks that erupt from volcanoes are called *extrusive* igneous rocks, simply because they are formed by the extrusion of magma onto the Earth's surface. Igneous rocks can also form deep underground, and these are called *intrusive* igneous rocks, because the magmas were intruded into pre-existing rocks and then slowly cooled. The reason why intrusive igneous rocks are now visible at the surface is that, over many millions of years, erosion has stripped away the overlying rocks. In this way, bodies of igneous rock that were once subterranean pools of magma are revealed at the surface. Some of these intrusions can be up to several kilometres across. In other cases, magma intruded pre-existing rocks to form long, slab-shaped bodies of igneous rock, with dimensions ranging from kilometres to slabs of no more than a few metres. These intrusions are called dykes in the case of vertical bodies, and sills in the case of horizontal bodies.

2.3.2 Texture of igneous rocks

What texture might you expect an igneous rock to have? An igneous rock contains crystals that grew as the magma cooled. Each crystal started to grow unhindered by neighbouring crystals, so an igneous rock therefore has a crystalline texture in which the crystals are randomly oriented.

To picture this, consider a magma, at an initial temperature of perhaps 1000 °C, as it slowly cools underground (Figure 2.3, path (a) to (d)). Initially the magma is completely molten (Figure 2.3a) but, unlike water placed in a freezer, magma does not turn from being totally liquid to totally solid at a single temperature when it is cooled. Instead, different minerals crystallise over a range of temperatures (in fact, over one or two hundred degrees Celsius). So, when the temperature of a magma falls by a small amount, only a few mineral crystals form (Figure 2.3b). On further cooling these crystals grow larger, and new minerals also start to crystallise (Figure 2.3c). Eventually, these crystals form an interlocking network, the last crystals to grow filling the spaces between those that have already formed. When completely solidified, the rock has the crystalline texture shown in Figure 2.3d.

In contrast, very fast cooling allows crystallisation to occur by the nucleation of many small crystals rather than the steady growth of a few crystals. The resulting igneous rock contains innumerable tiny crystals that may be so tiny as to be indistinguishable except under the high magnification of a microscope (Figure 2.3, path (a) to (e)). In the most extreme case, crystallisation is completely inhibited and the starting liquid is quenched to form volcanic glass.

■   Would you expect a fine-grained igneous rock to have formed deep below the Earth's surface or at the surface?

☐   A fine-grained igneous rock requires rapid cooling and this is more likely at the surface, where magma comes into contact with air or water, rather than in the hot interior of the Earth.

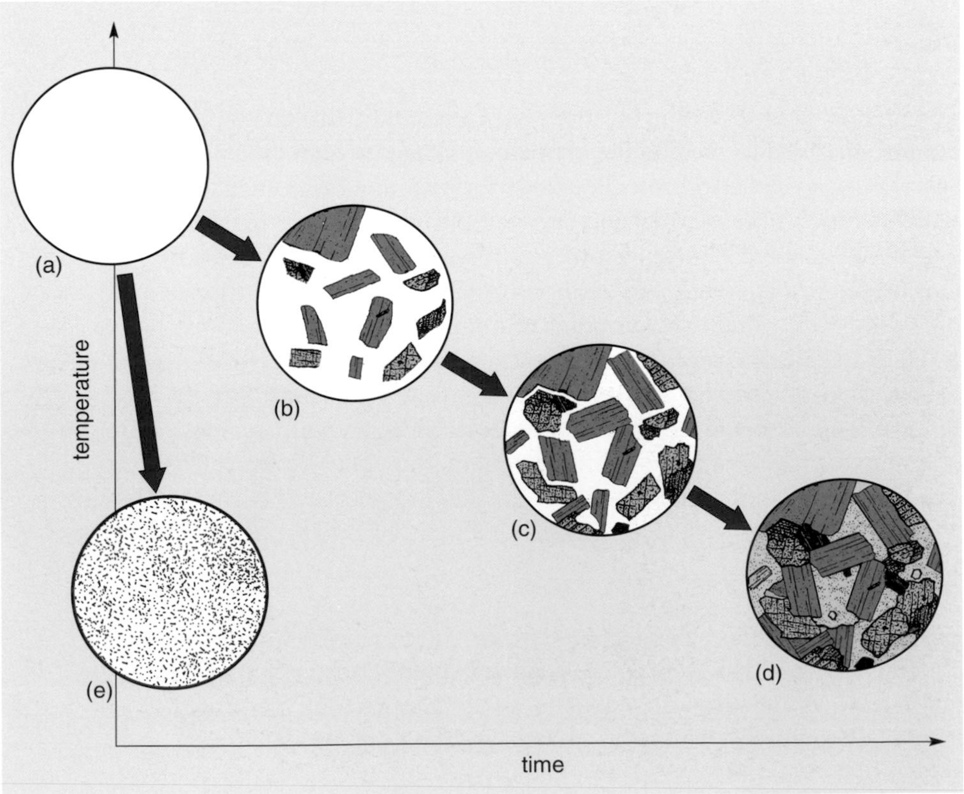

Figure 2.3   The number and size of crystals that grow in a magma depend on the temperature and the cooling rate. Starting with a liquid (a) that cools very slowly, the magma solidifies by the gradual growth of large crystals of different minerals (indicated by different patterns of shading) to produce an igneous rock with large crystals in random orientations (cooling path (a) to (d)). When cooling is fast, many very tiny crystals, rather than a few large crystals, grow with the result that a fine-grained igneous rock is formed (cooling path (a) to (e)).

In general, the number and size of the crystals in an igneous rock depend on the amount of time available for their growth. The slower the rate of cooling, the bigger the crystals will be. In the case of extrusive rocks, the amount of time is short – anything from a few seconds for droplets of magma flying through the air in an explosive volcanic eruption to a few years for the interior of a thick lava flow. This results in small crystals (Figure 2.3e). For intrusive rocks, the cooling rate is much slower and there is time for larger crystals to grow (Figure 2.3d). (The times involved are not known for certain because the magma at depth cannot be observed.)

Figure 2.4 illustrates this with two rocks of similar chemical composition, but from different igneous settings. Figure 2.4a shows an intrusive rock containing

Figure 2.4 Close-up views of rocks formed by the cooling of magma of the same chemical composition. (a) Gabbro formed by slow cooling in a subterranean magma chamber. (b) Basalt formed by rapid cooling of magma at the Earth's surface in a lava flow. The field of view is about 2.4 cm across in both views.

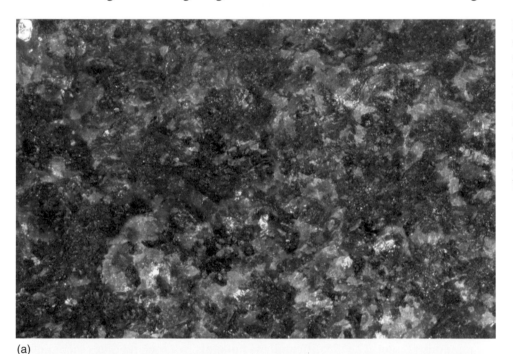

(a)

(b)

crystals of mainly two minerals: the dark one is the silicate-bearing iron (symbol Fe) and magnesium (Mg) mineral called **pyroxene**; the pale one is the silicate-bearing calcium (Ca), sodium (Na) and aluminium (Al) mineral called plagioclase **feldspar**. The crystals are intergrown (cf. Figure 2.3d) and easily visible. In contrast, Figure 2.4b shows a rock collected from a lava flow. This rock has only a few (pale) crystals that are large enough to see, which is because cooling and crystal growth were abruptly halted when the magma erupted and froze as lava. The rest of this rock is so fine-grained that the crystals are indistinguishable without the help of a microscope. However, there are a few small, round, dark areas (e.g. near the top left edge). These are gas bubbles, which formed when the magma rose to the surface and the gases that were dissolved in the magma came out of solution as the pressure on the magma decreased.

2.3.3 Chemical and mineral composition of igneous rocks

As well as varying in *grain size* (as a result of different cooling rates), igneous rocks also vary in *chemical composition* and hence in the identity and proportions of minerals present. For instance, the common igneous rock **granite** contains (as part of the strict geological definition of the term 'granite') between 10% and 35% by volume of the mineral quartz (chemical composition silicon dioxide: SiO_2). On the other hand, the igneous rock **gabbro** (Figure 2.4a) does not usually contain any quartz. This difference is due simply to the fact that granite contains a much higher proportion of the element silicon (Si) than gabbro does. So, chemical composition determines which minerals are present, and cooling rate determines the crystal size of those minerals.

2.3.4 Classifying igneous rocks

To classify (i.e. to name) igneous rocks, geologists use three pieces of information in combination: the grain size and the identity and the proportions of the minerals present. The identification of minerals in a rock involves recognising their particular distinguishing features. Such features include colour, **lustre** (how light is reflected from the mineral's surface) and shape. The way in which certain minerals break apart along preferred planes – a property called **cleavage** – can also be useful in identifying minerals because this property depends on how the mineral's constituent atoms are arranged. In some minerals the atoms are bound more strongly in some directions than in others, in which case there are natural planes of weakness present in the crystal. The mineral tends to break preferentially along these planes.

One mineral that shows this feature clearly is **mica**, a silicate mineral containing potassium (K), iron (Fe), magnesium (Mg) and aluminium (Al), together with hydroxyl (OH) groups. These compositional details need not concern you; the important point is that the potassium ions occur in layers, which separate sheets of more tightly bound silicon, oxygen and other atoms. Mica therefore splits apart parallel to the sheets, so has just one set of cleavage surfaces parallel to each other (Figure 2.5a). This is why mica forms platy or flake-like crystals, rather like the pages of a book. Other minerals can have two or three sets of cleavage (which intersect at characteristic angles) whereas others, notably quartz, have no cleavage and break irregularly.

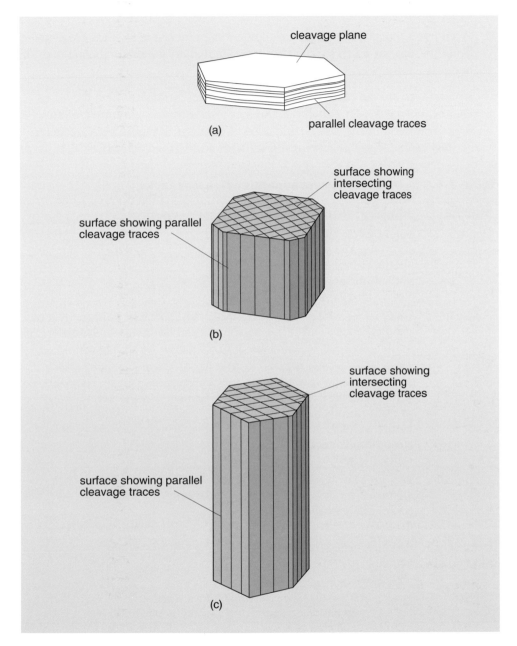

Figure 2.5   Examples of cleavage in different minerals. Note that in each case the number of cleavage traces with different directions depends on which face of the crystal is being looked at. (a) Mica: one set of cleavages when viewed edge on. (b) Pyroxene: two sets of cleavage intersecting at about 90° when viewed end on. (c) Amphibole: two sets of cleavage intersecting at about 120° when viewed end on. Table 2.1 gives additional information about these minerals, including their true colours.

Table 2.1 lists the most common silicate minerals found in igneous rocks (most of which are also common in sedimentary and metamorphic rocks). Minerals rich in silicon are towards the top, and those poorer in silicon, but richer in magnesium and iron, towards the bottom.

■ Would you expect an igneous rock containing a lot of magnesium (Mg) and iron (Fe), but not much silicon (Si), to contain all of the minerals in Table 2.1 in equal abundance?

☐ No: the type and proportions of the minerals present must reflect the chemical composition of the rock. So an igneous rock containing a relatively high proportion of Mg and Fe and a low amount of Si would be expected to contain more olivine and pyroxene and very little, if any, quartz.

Table 2.1 The common silicate minerals of igneous rocks.

Mineral	Diagnostic features	Chemical composition
Quartz	colourless to pale; glassy lustre (broken surfaces similar to broken glass); curved fractures; no visible internal structure	SiO_2
Feldspar	pale pink or white; two good cleavages	Ca, Na and Al silicates. Feldspar that is rich in Ca and Na is called plagioclase; if rich in K and Na, alkali feldspar.
Mica	forms platy crystals that split into flakes; one perfect cleavage. Brown or black mica is called biotite; colourless or silvery brown mica is called muscovite	K, Mg, Fe, Al silicate containing OH. Biotite is darker than muscovite because it contains more Mg and Fe.
Amphibole	dark green or black; elongated crystals with two cleavages (often hard to see)	Na, Ca, Mg, Fe and Al silicates with hydroxyl group
Pyroxene	dark green, dark brown or almost black; two good cleavages	Fe, Mg, Ca silicate
Olivine	grass green; no cleavage but has irregular fractures	Mg and Fe silicates

The variation in the mineral content of igneous rocks is shown in Figure 2.6, which provides the means of classifying igneous rocks. The percentage of each mineral present is represented on the vertical scale, and the range of rock type (effectively the chemical composition) is given on the horizontal scale. Coarse-grained rocks (typical grain size greater than 2 mm) are named separately from fine-grained rocks (typical grain size less than 0.25 mm). Note that the proportion of pale-coloured minerals (felsic minerals) increases from left to right, reflecting the increase in the concentration of silicon in the chemical composition of the rocks. According to the diagram, granite is defined as a coarse-grained igneous rock containing quartz, feldspar (both alkali and plagioclase), mica and sometimes **amphibole**. The relative proportions of these different minerals are given by the width of the appropriate band on the diagram. For instance, the quartz content of granite can range from about 10% to 35%, and the mica content from about 5% to 15%.

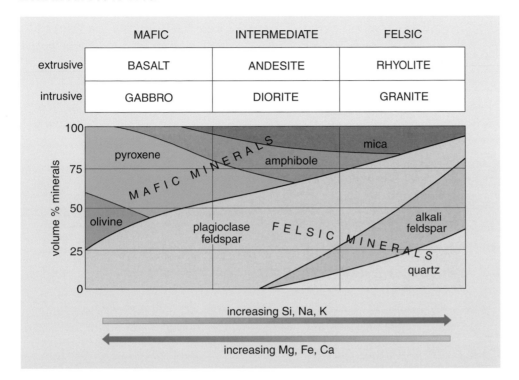

Figure 2.6   Classification of common coarse- and fine-grained igneous rocks according to variation in mineral content. The vertical scale shows proportions in per cent of minerals and the horizontal scale shows the range of rock types. Dark-coloured minerals are called mafic minerals (they are rich in *ma*gnesium and iron, *F*e). Pale minerals are called felsic minerals (from *fel*dspar and *si*licon). The arrows below the diagram show how the content of certain elements varies across the compositional range of common igneous rocks.

Extrusive and intrusive rocks of the same composition have different names:

- Extrusive mafic rock is **basalt** and intrusive mafic rock is gabbro.
- Extrusive intermediate rock is **andesite** and intrusive intermediate rock is **diorite**.
- Extrusive felsic rock is **rhyolite** and intrusive felsic rock is granite.

The volume percentage of minerals is shown as fields where the percentage present can be read from the *y*-axis and the rock's classification along the *x*-axis. Mafic minerals (**olivine**, pyroxene, amphibole and mica) occupy the top left of the diagram and felsic minerals (plagioclase and alkali feldspar and quartz) occupy the bottom right.

Figure 2.4 shows that:

- Mafic rocks all contain pyroxene; some may contain olivine and/or amphibole and/or mica.
- Intermediate rocks all contain plagioclase feldspar, amphibole and mica; some may contain pyroxene and others may contain alkali feldspar and quartz.

- Felsic rocks all contain plagioclase feldspar, alkali feldspar, quartz and mica; some may contain amphibole.

- If the percentages of minerals in a rock are known then the rock can be classified using the scale on the diagram.

Question 2.1

Do igneous rocks with small crystals form at the Earth's surface?

Give reasons for your answer.

Note: the answer to this question and others raised in the text are provided in a section at the end of this book.

Question 2.2

Look at Figure 2.6 and decide which of the following statements are true.

(a) Granite does not contain olivine.

(b) The proportion of pyroxene in gabbro can vary from about 25% to 50%.

(c) Alkali feldspar is more abundant than plagioclase feldspar in coarse-grained igneous rocks.

(d) A coarse-grained igneous rock containing 60% plagioclase, 15% pyroxene, 15% amphibole and 10% mica is classified as diorite.

(e) A coarse-grained igneous rock containing 50% plagioclase, 35% pyroxene and 15% amphibole is classified as gabbro.

(f) Amphibole can be present in gabbro, diorite and granite.

2.4 The formation of sedimentary rocks

2.4.1 Sedimentary material

The laying down, or deposition, of layers of rock fragments, mineral grains and biological material, such as the shells or other hard parts of dead organisms, can produce sedimentary rocks. Once deposited, the loose, unconsolidated sediment may be converted into a solid rock by compaction and cementing of the grains together by chemical action deep below the surface. Therefore, these rocks consist of fragments of sedimentary material, bound together by even smaller fragments, or a type of cementing material, thus displaying a fragmental texture, as shown in Figure 2.7.

2.4.2 Sedimentary processes

Sedimentary grains are formed when the rocks at the Earth's surface are slowly broken up physically by exposure to wind and frost, and decomposed (chemically) by rainwater or biological action. These processes are collectively

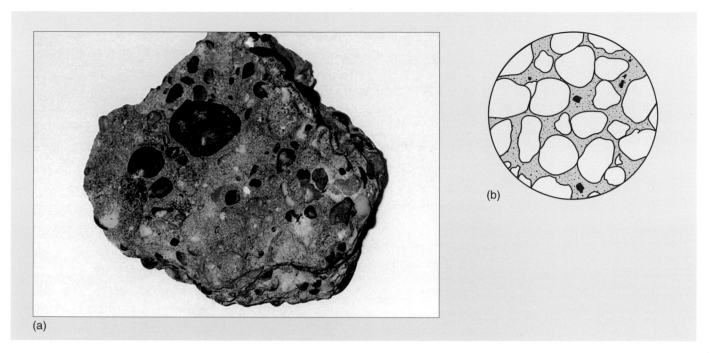

Figure 2.7   The fragmental texture of sedimentary rocks: (a) a sample of conglomerate, about 20 cm across, comprising rounded pebbles and enclosing sand grains; (b) a generalised sketch showing round grains bound together by much smaller grains.

termed **weathering**. Once a rock has been broken up by weathering, the small rock fragments and individual mineral grains can be eroded from their place of origin by water, wind or ice and transported to be deposited elsewhere as roughly horizontal layers of sediment. The resulting sediment reflects the original rock types that were weathered; the efficiency of erosion and transport; the extents of chemical and physical degradation of the sediment grains during transport; and the conditions under which the grains were deposited from the transporting water, wind or ice. For example, sand-sized grains of quartz are one of the main constituents of sandstone, but those grains may have been transported by water in a river, or carried by waves on a seashore, or blown around in hot desert sandstorms (to give just three possibilities). How might you distinguish which of the many transport possibilities is the most likely in any given case?

One approach is to use the size and shape of the grains in a sediment or sedimentary rock to reveal details about sediment's origin. For example, a vigorous river transports much larger grains than a gentle current in a lake, so the size of the grains indicates the strength of the currents that could have transported and deposited the grains. In other words, the grain size depends on the energy of the environment in which the sediment was deposited. The general shape of the grains tells you about the nature of the transporting medium: for example, was it water or air? (See Box 2.2.)

Box 2.2 A story in a grain of sand

Quartz is a hard mineral that is very common in the Earth's continental crust. It is resistant to attack by chemicals and is physically strong, so it tends to survive the weathering process that disaggregates and decomposes pre-existing rocks. Many sedimentary rocks contain grains of quartz. These are recognisable by their glassy appearance (particularly on freshly broken surfaces) and lack of cleavage. Quartz is also hard enough to scratch steel.

Whether quartz grains are transported and deposited by moving air (by being blown around by the winds in a desert) or by moving water (in a river or in ocean currents) determines how rounded they become (Figure 2.8). The degree of rounding of quartz grains depends on the intensity and frequency with which grains collide with each other, and these factors depend on the environmental conditions. Air is less viscous than water, so wind-blown quartz grains collide more violently than quartz grains carried in water, which has a cushioning effect. Also, the wind speeds needed to move a sand grain of a given size are higher than the speeds for flowing water. This means that collisions between grains are much more energetic in air than in water, so the corners of wind-blown grains are readily knocked off, and the grains are usually far more rounded (Figure 2.8b) than water-transported grains (Figure 2.8a).

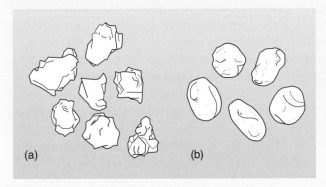

(a)   (b)

Figure 2.8 Examples of variation in grain shape associated with difference in sedimentary environment: (a) river sand (×20); (b) wind-blown sand (×20).

■ Are all sediments composed of fragments of rock and minerals eroded from pre-existing rocks?

☐ No: some sedimentary rocks also contain the remains of dead organisms, i.e. fossilised plants or animals that were living when the sedimentary material was deposited.

Any record of ancient life preserved in a rock is called a **fossil**. Sometimes fossils are rare, whereas a few rocks are composed of virtually nothing else *but* fossils. In particular, many limestones were formed by the accumulation of the calcite (calcium carbonate, $CaCO_3$) shells and skeletons of marine organisms. **Chalk** is a well-known type of limestone that outcrops extensively across southern England; it is almost pure calcite, and consists largely of minute calcite plates of countless fossils of planktonic algae (called **phytoplankton**). Other limestones, such as those in the Peak District of northern England, contain abundant fossils of reef-building corals. Another example of a biologically formed sedimentary rock is coal, a carbon-rich material that is formed from compressed layers of woody plants.

Fossils are important when reconstructing the geological past because they are records of the environment at the time and place the fossilised organisms were living. For instance, limestones rich in corals typically indicate warm, shallow seas – the conditions needed for a coral reef ecosystem to thrive.

It is important that as many lines of evidence as possible are used to give a consistent interpretation of a rock's origin. No single feature should be taken as unequivocally diagnostic. For instance, think of a desert sand, composed of well-rounded, red oxide-coated, well-sorted quartz grains. Now imagine that climatic conditions change and these sand grains are swept away by flowing rivers and re-deposited elsewhere. The new sand deposit is produced by the action of flowing water, but the sand grains may retain many of the characteristics of wind deposition inherited from their previous history. The interpretation can be misleading if other lines of evidence are ignored. Supplementary evidence could come from any fossils in the rock and the nature of adjacent sedimentary layers. Getting all of the necessary information involves a mixture of making observations and measurements at rock exposures in the field and examining and analysing samples in the laboratory.

Wind-blown sand deposited in desert environments differs from water-deposited sand in another way. Quartz sand grains in a desert often have a coating of red or orange iron oxide. This red-orange coloration is typical of desert landscapes and it is derived from the insoluble 'rusty' residue from weathering of iron-rich minerals. Water-deposited sand grains lack such an obvious coating.

The degree of sorting in a sediment is another useful method for distinguishing different types of depositional situation. **Sorting** is a measure of the *range* of grain sizes present in a sediment or sedimentary rock. A poorly sorted sediment (Figure 2.9a) has a wide range of grain sizes as a result of rapid deposition, such as occurs during a storm. On the other hand, a well-sorted sediment has a narrow range of grain sizes (Figure 2.9c), and is the result of extensive reworking of a sediment by wind action in deserts, or wave action on beaches and in shallow shelf seas.

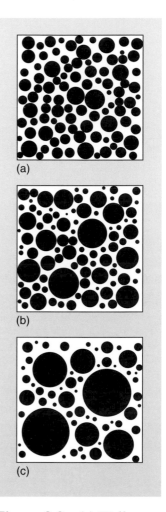

Figure 2.9   (a) Well-sorted sediment; (b) moderately sorted sediment; (c) poorly sorted sediment.

2.4.3 Sedimentary strata

You have seen that the detective work of piecing together a part of Earth's history from sedimentary rocks involves the detailed investigation of rock samples, but this gives only a partial picture. On the larger scale of a rock exposure, there can be plenty to see and interpret. As you will see at the Residential School, sedimentary rocks are usually found as layers called **strata** (Figure 2.10), each stratum (layer) recording the particular conditions at the time of its deposition. (Note: sedimentary layers are often called 'beds' but, strictly speaking, the term

bed is reserved for strata thicker than 1 cm; thinner layers are called laminae, singular lamina.) Over time, conditions might have changed, either gradually or quickly, changing the nature of the sediment being deposited. In this way, a vertical stack of sedimentary strata is a record of changing conditions during a segment of geological time. The oldest sediments are at the bottom, with progressively younger strata laid down on top. Geologists refer to this as the principle of **superposition**: older rocks are overlain by younger rocks; an individual layer is younger than the one beneath it and older than the one above it; the oldest layer is at the bottom. This provides a relative timescale. Changes in sedimentary rocks (or in the types of fossil they may contain) up through a sequence of strata provide a record of changing conditions over the period of time during which the rocks were deposited.

Figure 2.10   A succession of sedimentary strata (layers) exposed in a cliff on the Dorset coast in southern England.

2.4.4 Stratigraphy and geological time

Stratigraphy is the study of how the types of strata have varied over time and how they are distributed geographically. One of the most useful results of stratigraphy is a generalised geological succession – the **stratigraphic column** – that defines the divisions of geological time. Figure 2.11 shows the geological timescale. The broadest division of Earth's history is into two intervals (called eons) of very different length: the Precambrian Eon and the Phanerozoic Eon. The Precambrian is a vast amount of time – from the origin of the Earth, 4600 million years (or Ma, which stands for mega-annum) ago, to the start of the Phanerozoic, 545 Ma ago. The Precambrian is also informally known as the 'Cryptozoic', which is derived from the Greek words meaning 'hidden life'. This is the period of time when organisms did not have hard parts such as shells, so it is difficult to find their remains in sedimentary rocks. In contrast, 'Phanerozoic' is derived from the Greek words meaning 'visible life', reflecting the great abundance of fossils derived from the hard parts of organisms throughout this eon. The Phanerozoic Eon is divided into three **eras**: the Palaeozoic, Mesozoic and Cenozoic Eras (meaning 'ancient life', 'middle life', and 'recent life', respectively). Each era is divided into several **periods** of unequal length (Figure 2.11). The current period, which started 1.8 Ma ago, is the Quaternary Period.

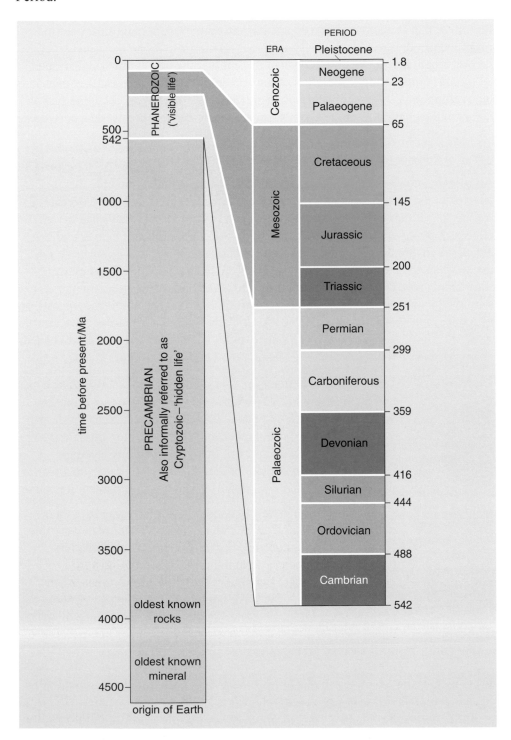

Figure 2.11   The geological timescale.

Looking at Figure 2.11, you might think that there is a complete sequence of rocks everywhere, but there is not; in the same way there are no historical records for certain times from certain areas. In the field, an Earth scientist might find rocks of, say, the Triassic Period lying above and in direct contact with rocks of the Carboniferous Period, so that rock evidence for the Permian Period is not present. This means that either there was no deposition of sediment during the Permian Period, or that these rocks were deposited, and then eroded, before rocks of the Triassic Period were laid down. This type of relationship in the geological rock record, where at a contact point beds of the intervening age are missing, is called an **unconformity**. The recognition of unconformities in the field is a key part of unravelling the geological history of an area because they represent some sort of hiatus in the conditions at the Earth's surface where the sediments were deposited.

2.4.5 Fossils and ancient environments

An essential component of any environment is the plant and animal life that is adapted to the prevailing conditions. Fossilised plants and animals are therefore wonderful sources of information about ancient environments. Plants can leave remains ranging from roots, leaves and twigs to seeds and pollen. Leaves and twigs are relatively fragile, and require a comparatively low energy environment (e.g. the mudflats of an estuary) for their preservation. Seeds, pollen and spores are surprisingly robust, and are often the only parts of a plant to survive. Animals can be preserved in one of two ways: either by a part of their body remaining as a fossil, or by a trace, such as footprints preserved in a muddy sediment becoming preserved as sedimentary rock (a trace fossil). Even dung can end up fossilised, the resulting fossils being called coprolites (Figure 2.12).

Body fossils of animals include shells, skeletal frameworks, bones and teeth. There is not space here to describe the most common fossil groups; however, you will be able to find examples during your Residential School that can be discussed in your tutor group. Figure 2.13 illustrates some of them and their characteristic features. It is more important here to consider *how* an organism is fossilised, and what it can tell us about the environment it lived in.

First, consider the organism itself. Does it have any hard parts? If not (e.g. a jellyfish) then its chances of fossilisation are very low. However, some soft-bodied organisms burrow into sediment (e.g. lugworms, which leave the familiar worm casts on seashores), and there is a chance that their burrows become preserved as trace fossils. An organism with a one-piece shell, such as a periwinkle or garden snail, has a better chance of being preserved intact than if its skeleton is made up of many pieces, such as a sea urchin or crinoid (Figure 2.12c).

Figure 2.12 A 10 cm long coprolite from Dorset, which provides trace fossil evidence of a crocodile-like marine animal that lived during the Jurassic Period. The original organic material has been replaced, after burial, by crystals of iron pyrites (FeS_2), sometimes called 'fool's gold', which can be seen glinting at either end.

■ Which of the following indicates deposition in a high-energy environment, and which in a low-energy environment?
(a) A sedimentary layer containing complete examples of thin, fragile shells.
(b) A sedimentary layer containing broken shell fragments.

☐ Broken shells (b) indicate a high-energy environment, whereas fragile shells can remain intact (a) only if the speed of the transporting and the depositing currents is low (i.e. a low-energy environment).

Fossils of land-dwelling organisms (e.g. Figure 2.13b) indicate deposition in or at least near a terrestrial environment, whereas marine fossils indicate a marine environment suitable for the fossil organisms to have lived in (e.g. correct temperature range, light levels, salinity, water depth). This evidence can then be added to evidence from the features of sedimentary grains (Section 2.4.2) to help reconstruct the environment.

2.4.6 Sedimentary structures

Consider some of the places where sedimentary materials are moved and deposited. Are the sediments always laid down in perfectly horizontal and flat layers? No: as often as not, the depositing surface is not perfectly flat. Instead,

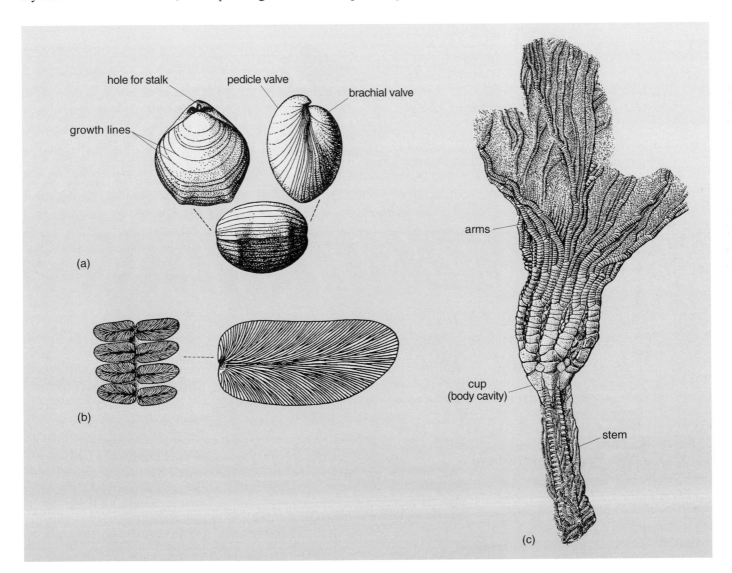

Figure 2.13 Three types of fossil: (a) the shell of a member of the group of marine animals called brachiopods (*Obovothris*, from the Jurassic Period), life size; (b) fragment of a land plant (*Neuropteris*, from the Carboniferous Period), half life size, with detail shown at ×2.5 life size; (c) upper part of a crinoid (*Pentacrinites*, from the Jurassic Period), a member of the group of marine animals which includes sea urchins (×1; but some specimens are much larger).

a system of parallel ridges, or ripple marks, like the ones in Figure 2.14a, form by the action that flowing water has on the erosion, transport and deposition of sand grains. In sedimentary strata, ripples and dunes (which are effectively larger versions of ripple marks) are normally seen in cross-section rather than in plan view, because pristine depositional surfaces are rarely exposed. In cross-section, the thin sedimentary layers that built up each ripple or dune can be visible, inclined at an angle to the top and bottom of the bed as a whole (Figure 2.14b). This feature is called **cross-stratification** and it is a clue to the strength, direction and setting of the currents that produced them.

Figure 2.14   (a) Ripple marks on a sandy beach. (b) Cross-stratification in sandstone formed by underwater dunes advancing from right to left; the exposure is about 3 m high.

(a)

(b)

Many features associated with either erosion or deposition in a sedimentary environment can be preserved. For instance, desert dunes can have cross-stratification on a scale of many metres. All such structures are called sedimentary structures and, as we have just seen, provide evidence with which to interpret ancient sedimentary environments. At the Residential School you may have an opportunity to see sedimentary structures forming on beaches.

Question 2.3

Explain whether the energy of the environment of deposition of the following sediments is (i) high, (ii) medium or (iii) low.

(a) A sediment made up of pebbles and boulders.

(b) A sediment made up of fine clay particles.

(c) A sediment made up of sand grains.

2.5   The formation of metamorphic rocks

Any type of rock can become a metamorphic rock if it is heated to temperatures of several hundred degrees Celsius (°C), and/or if it is subjected to high pressure (caused by the weight of overlying rocks). During **metamorphism**, the minerals in the rock become chemically unstable, meaning that their constituent ions are redistributed. The result is that either large crystals grow at the expense of existing smaller ones, or a new set of minerals is formed. In general, the overall chemical composition of the rock remains about the same. Although igneous and metamorphic rocks both form at high temperatures, an important distinction is that metamorphism occurs in the solid state, whereas igneous activity involves liquid rock (magma).

2.5.1 Causes of metamorphism

■ Which natural process could heat up a rock?

☐ Heating is caused when hot magma intrudes into a cool rock.

On the other hand, there is an increase in both pressure and temperature if the rock becomes more deeply buried as a result of Earth movements, particularly at convergent plate boundaries where continents collide, or is covered by a deepening layer of sedimentary deposits.

Therefore, metamorphic rocks are found in two settings. In the first and simplest setting a narrow zone around the edge of an igneous intrusion is heated by the magma and undergoes metamorphic recrystallisation. This is called contact metamorphism because it is caused by hot magma coming into contact with cold rocks; contact metamorphism is caused by heating alone.

The second common setting of metamorphism is far more extensive, and is caused by the deep burial of crust at continental collision zones. In this setting, huge volumes of rock experience increases in temperature and pressure, causing metamorphism on a regional scale; this is called regional metamorphism.

2.5.2 Metamorphic recrystallisation

To consider metamorphic recrystallisation at its simplest level, imagine a sedimentary rock composed entirely of quartz grains, i.e. a quartz sandstone. Sandstone is a sedimentary rock and so has a fragmental texture (see Figure 2.7b). When it is subjected to high temperature and high pressure new minerals cannot form because there are no other minerals present that the quartz grains could react with. All that can happen is that the quartz grains recrystallise and the rock quartzite is formed. The original fragmental texture is obliterated and replaced by a crystalline texture. Likewise, when a pure limestone comprising calcite (i.e. $CaCO_3$) is metamorphosed the calcite recrystallises, and marble is produced. In these cases, the rock adjusts to a high pressure or temperature by slowly recrystallising in a denser, more compact form.

However, most cases see a rock containing several different minerals, giving a richer chemical mix for metamorphic reactions to work with. At sufficiently high temperature or pressure, the original minerals react with each other, and new mineral crystals grow. For this to happen the constituent atoms must diffuse at different rates through the rock, but diffusion is extremely slow so atoms can move only very short distances in a given amount of time. The chemical rearrangement of the rock therefore entails the growth of small crystals, unless the temperature is particularly high, in which case larger crystals can grow. Whenever metamorphism occurs in the compressional environment of continental collision zones (regional metamorphism), the rock is also subject to directed pressure, which also affects the way the minerals crystallise. In the case of the metamorphism of mudrocks, mica crystals are formed during metamorphism. Mica crystals are characteristically platy in shape, reflecting the fact that the atoms in mica are arranged in layers or sheets (see Section 2.3.4). When platy minerals grow during metamorphism, the energetically most favourable pattern of growth is one in which their flat surfaces lie more or less parallel, and at right angles to the main direction of imposed pressure (Figure 2.15). Likewise, any elongated crystals grow aligned parallel with each other.

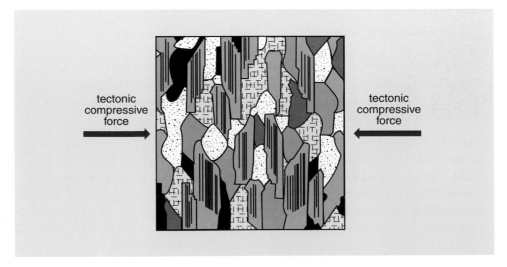

Figure 2.15   Sketch of the interlocking crystalline texture in a metamorphic rock formed by regional metamorphism; mineral banding develops at right angles to the direction of compression.

■ In what way is the metamorphic texture shown in Figure 2.15 the same as the texture in igneous rocks (Figure 2.3) and in what way does it differ?

☐ Metamorphic rock has a crystalline texture, like igneous rocks. However, it also has mineral layering, or alignment, whereas the crystals in igneous rocks grew in random directions.

The alignment of platy minerals means that the rock has a series of closely spaced planes of weakness running through it, so it tends to split apart into fairly flat pieces. The rock is said to have a **foliation** because its mineral grains are aligned like a stack of leaves (foliage) lying one on top of the other. A classic example is **slate**, a metamorphic rock with an extremely fine grain size that can be split into thin sheets, which are used for roofing. Slate, and the coarser-grained metamorphic rock **schist** (pronounced 'shh-ist', to rhyme with 'mist') (Figure 2.16), have marked foliation because they contain a lot of mica. However, not all metamorphic rocks are as rich in mica. In these cases metamorphism can still produce a banding effect but the minerals grow segregated into alternating bands a few millimetres to centimetres thick. Bands of light-coloured minerals alternate with bands of dark-coloured minerals, and the rock is called **gneiss** (pronounced 'nice'). In general, the coarser the grain size of a metamorphic rock, the higher the temperature and/or pressure.

Figure 2.16 The metamorphic rock schist. The darker platy mica crystals are arranged in undulating layers, defining a foliation. The sample is about 6 cm long.

■ Is the control of grain size in metamorphic rocks the same as in igneous rocks?

☐ No: in igneous rocks, grain size is controlled by cooling rate (and crystals grow from a liquid); the slower the cooling, the coarser the grain size. In metamorphic rocks, grain size is controlled by pressure and temperature (and crystals grow by the transformation of existing minerals in the solid state); the higher the temperature and pressure, the coarser the grain size.

The end product of metamorphism depends on two main variables: the chemical composition of the starting rock, and the pressure and temperature conditions under which metamorphism occurred. A useful analogy is cooking: the product of baking in an oven depends on the ingredients that went in (the chemical composition) and the temperature that the ingredients were subjected to in the oven. Just as the shape, colour and taste of food from an oven gives you clues about the ingredients and the baking conditions, so the texture and mineralogy of a metamorphic rock indicate something about the original rock type and the temperature and pressure conditions in the crust where metamorphism occurred.

Question 2.4

Compare and contrast contact metamorphism and regional metamorphism in terms of (a) the presence of foliation and (b) the distribution of the affected rocks.

2.6   Interlude

Now that the features of igneous, sedimentary and metamorphic rocks have been described, and you have seen how these features can be explained by the processes that formed the rocks, this is a useful point to take a break before continuing with the next section. Before returning to it, you could see for yourself which types of rock there are in your local area. Can you identify their texture or find any fossils? Surfaces that are not obscured by grime or lichens are by far the best, as it is the attributes of the rock itself, not any later weathering processes, that are of interest. Polished work surfaces, ornamental stones, grave stones and shop fronts are interesting possibilities to start with. Avoid rocks with a grain size so small that you cannot recognise individual grains; you need a microscope to study those rocks!

When studying rocks, bear in mind the following points.

- Careful observation is one of the fundamental aspects of doing science and involves more than casual 'looking'.
- Consider what you are looking at; questions may occur to you during observation and you may be able to find the answers by looking more carefully.
- Observe systematically and purposefully: bear in mind the types of features you may see.
- Observe thoroughly – that splendid fossil may be just around the corner!
- Use your prior knowledge to help guide your search.
- Remember that scientific observation should be thoughtful, focused, methodical and well informed.
- Take care not to destroy evidence – leave exposures as you find them for those who come after you. Collect only from loose material.

Now is a good time to skim through Sections 1 to 3 of the workbook for Activity A. You won't be able to make sense of all of it without the hand specimens of rocks. Don't worry about this – we just want you to get an idea about what is expected of you.

In the next section you will do an activity that introduces some of the geological skills and ideas that you will develop in Activity C 'Investigating the environment'.

2.7   Geological fieldwork

Although you can learn from rock samples in a laboratory or at home, the 'natural habitat' of rocks is outdoors. Here the distribution and layout of different rocks are visible wherever rocks are exposed in places such as riverbeds, cliffs, rocky shorelines, quarries and road cuttings. The exposed rocks can be studied in just the same detail as individual laboratory samples. Geological fieldwork also allows the size and extent of each rock unit to be seen and the relationships between them to be observed. This gives more information from which to deduce the conditions in which the exposed rocks might have formed.

You might not have looked closely at a rock exposure before, so you will be guided through this aspect of scientific fieldwork in Activity C 'Investigating the environment'. To deduce the conditions in which the rocks formed and the sequence of geological events that formed them, you will make making systematic observations and record those observations in the Activity C workbook. This will give you the basic information from which to work out some of the geological history of the area you will visit.

2.7.1   Making and using field sketches

How do you start to make sense of a rock exposure? Drawing a sketch is one of the best ways to start, as it forces you to notice many aspects of the exposure. It also helps you to build up a picture of which aspects are significant and which are incidental or even irrelevant to a geological study. The aim of a field sketch is to provide a record of your observations (along with notes taken at the same time and perhaps a photograph to record the details). A sketch is complementary to a photograph because it allows you to highlight and label the significant features. However, your sketch need not be a work of art!

Activity 2.1   Sketching a geological exposure

Suggested study time: 15 minutes

Look at Figure 2.17a: a photograph of a coastal rock exposure of sedimentary strata. The rock is far from featureless, and you will explore the visible features by first sketching the exposure, and then working through your sketched observations to develop some ideas about the history of the rocks. Figure 2.17b provides space for you to draw your sketch of the main features of the coastal exposure. Use a pencil, and follow the general guidelines below. Spend no more than 15 minutes doing this.

1   Spend a minute or so looking carefully at the rock face to begin to recognise some general details.

2   Now it is time to start committing some of your observations to paper! Draw in the skyline and the base of the exposure. (In Figure 2.17a this extends to the bottom of the photograph.) This marks out the area that you need to concentrate on.

3   Sketch in the main features using simple lines wherever possible. If necessary, rub out and redraw particular areas until you are happy with them. Part of the skill of making successful geological observations of complex exposures is to follow any key feature (e.g. the top or bottom of a sedimentary bed), as far as you can with your eye until it disappears from view. Similarly, the skill of making an effective geological sketch is to draw a discrete, continuous

line (where the feature is continuous), rather than to sketch a vague series of unconnected lines. Ignore shadows from sunlight and features such as loose boulders, fallen branches, etc. You can indicate any patches of vegetation using simple symbols for grass, trees, etc.

4   Label the features you have drawn.

5   Add a scale, the approximate orientation (e.g. by marking west on the left and east on the right), and a title which includes the location.

When you have finished, compare your sketch with the one in the answer section at the end of this book (Figure 2.21), which was drawn by another student, and also compare Figure 2.21 with Figure 2.17a.

Figure 2.17 (a) View of a coastal rock exposure, about 10 m high, looking roughly north; west is to the left and east is to the right. (b) Space for your pencil sketch of the rock exposure.

(a)

(b)

2.7.2 Interpreting a geological exposure

We now want you to use your observations from sketching the exposure. It is helpful to start by briefly summarising the main features. First, you probably noticed the large boulder in the foreground of Figure 2.17a. Where did it come from? It seems to be the same colour as nearby rocks, so most likely came from the same piece of coastline. However, because the boulder is not a part of the solid bedrock, you cannot rely on it to give a true picture of the local bedrock. Boulders and any other loose rocks might have been transported by natural processes or human activities, so geologists usually ignore them when investigating the rocks exposed at the surface. Indeed, much of Britain has been affected by glaciation with the result that the countryside is strewn with large boulders derived from far and wide and transported by moving ice – great for reconstructing the routes of past glaciers but a shoal of red herrings when trying to investigate the underlying bedrock! Therefore, ignore the boulder and concentrate on the rocks forming the solid cliffs and foreground.

The exposed rocks have sets of parallel lines running through them, which might have been one of the first features you spotted when looking carefully at the photograph. These lines define sedimentary layers or strata, which means these are sedimentary rocks. In the rocks forming most of the vertical cliff face, the layers are horizontal whereas in the white rocks of the foreground, the layers are inclined to the right. They are like a tilted stack of books. In this case, the strata slope, or dip, to the right at an angle of about 30°. The outcrop has two distinct parts: the upper set of horizontal strata and the lower part of dipping strata.

Looking first at the dipping strata, the sediments appear fairly monotonous, with no obvious change in colour or thickness of individual beds as you look from left to right. Close up, the rock has a pitted or pock-marked appearance in places (e.g. the rock face immediately to the right of the large boulder). However, this is a superficial feature caused by weathering of the rock where it is exposed to the elements. The cement holding the sedimentary grains together may not be uniform, such that weathering and erosion are uneven, resulting in the weakest spots becoming pock-marked. Although this is an interesting feature, it is a detail that you need not consider further.

The horizontal strata are also a pale colour, although the vertical cliff that they form has some areas of black and pale green coloration. Rock faces that have been exposed for a long time often become discoloured, through chemical weathering or colonisation by lichens and other organisms. In this case, the black coloration is a result of biological activity, and the natural colour of the rock is visible in only a few places. Green algae are growing on the lower part of the cliff where wave action provides moisture. When working at the rock exposure, an Earth scientist would carefully use a geological hammer to break open the rock and expose a fresh, unweathered surface in order to discover the true nature of the rock.

As well as spotting the fairly continuous horizontal lines defining the horizontal strata (or bedding), you might also have recognised that there are several sharp, nearly vertical 'cracks' running through the rocks. These cracks or **fractures** in the rock are planes of weakness called **joints**. The rocks on either side of each

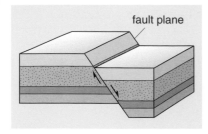

fault plane

Figure 2.18   Example of how sedimentary strata are displaced by fault movement. The arrows show the direction in which the strata each side of the fault plane have moved.

joint have not been displaced, which distinguishes joints from faults. A **fault** is a fracture across which there has been movement, such that the rocks on either side of the fault have been systematically shifted up, down or sideways (Figure 2.18). Joints can form as a mechanical response to the decrease in pressure when deeply buried rocks are exhumed by the erosion of a great thickness of overlying rocks. Faults are formed when rocks break and move because of compression or stretching, with movement on either side of the fault relieving the pent-up compression or tension.

Lastly, look at the junction, or contact, between the lower dipping strata and the upper horizontal strata of Figure 2.17a.

■   What is the shape of the contact between the dipping and horizontal strata?

☐   The contact is more or less horizontal, but with some undulations of up to about 1 m in amplitude on the left- and right-hand sides of the exposure. The cliff has become incised through preferential erosion along this contact.

2.7.3   Explaining the observations

Having made and reviewed your observations, you are now in a position to interpret them. Why are the rocks the way they are? The sedimentary strata in Figure 2.17a were probably deposited in essentially horizontal layers, so why is one set tilted and the other horizontal? To answer this, you need to consider the processes that account for each feature and the relative timings of these processes. So, the strata exposed below the cliff have been deposited and tilted. The strata exposed high in the cliff have been deposited but not tilted. The rocks with the more complicated history must be the older of the two sets of strata.

The following sequence of events accounts for these observations.

1   Deposition of sediments as horizontal layers. (Details about the environment in which these strata were deposited could be discovered by closer study of the rocks, by observing the nature of the grains, sedimentary structure or fossils, as you saw in Section 2.4.)

2   Compaction and cementation of the white sediments to form solid sedimentary rock.

3   Tilting of the white strata. This could have been through powerful movements in the Earth, involving the rocks being compressed from the sides, to produce folds (Figure 2.19).

■   Assuming that the rocks were not completely overturned, in which direction (left or right) would you walk to find the youngest tilted strata?

☐   The youngest layers lie on top of older layers (the principle of superposition, which was introduced in Section 2.4.3), so these are on the far right in Figure 2.17a.

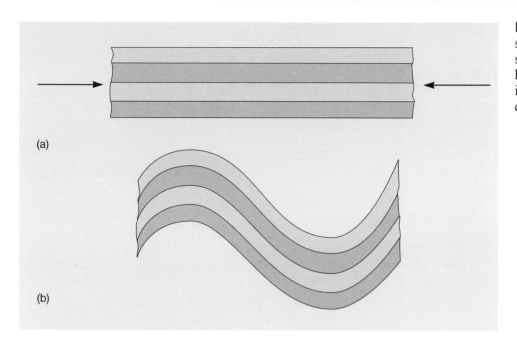

Figure 2.19   Diagram showing how initially horizontal strata (a) may be folded and hence tilted. (b) The arrows in (a) show the direction of compression.

(a)

(b)

4   Weathering and erosion to expose the tilted white strata at the Earth's surface, before deposition of the younger strata.

5   Deposition of sediment onto the uneven, eroded surface of tilted white strata. The hummocky contact between the two sets of strata that you saw at the end of Section 2.7.2 is, therefore, the original land (or sea-floor) surface when the younger strata were first deposited.

■   Which term describes the contact between the tilted and the horizontal strata?

☐   It is called an unconformity (Section 2.4.4).

6   Compaction and cementation of the younger sediments to form solid sedimentary rock.

7   Formation of vertical joints in the horizontal strata.

8   Erosion to produce the present land surface and coastal exposure.

2.8   The rock cycle

While you are reading this, rocks are being formed and destroyed on the Earth. Rocks are being heated and squeezed to form new metamorphic rocks; other rocks are melting to form magmas, which eventually cool and solidify as new igneous rocks; and the processes of weathering, erosion, transport and deposition are generating new sediments. The continuous action of rock-forming processes means that (given time) any rock in the Earth's crust will be transformed into a new type of rock and these may also be transformed into yet other rocks. This recycling of rock materials is called the **rock cycle**.

2.8.1 Moving around the rock cycle

One way of illustrating the possible ways of moving material around the rock cycle is to draw a diagram that places the processes in their geological contexts. Since the rock cycle involves processes occurring both on the Earth's surface and within its interior, a cross-section through the Earth's crust and uppermost **mantle** is used, as shown in Figure 2.19. This diagram highlights the most common processes in the rock cycle.

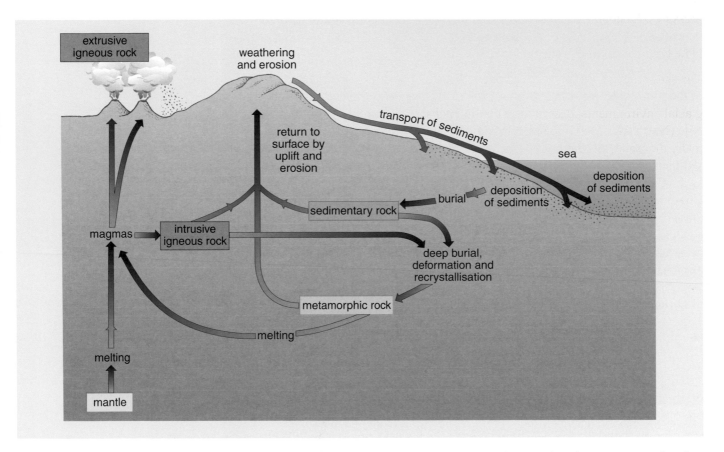

Figure 2.20   The rock cycle. The arrows show the paths taken and the processes in transforming one type of rock (boxed text) into another type.

Mantle rock (from below the crust) melts and rises into the crust as magma. Here it may crystallise as intrusive igneous rock or be erupted at volcanoes as extrusive igneous rock.

Intrusive igneous rock and the other (sedimentary and metamorphic) rocks in the crust are exposed at the surface when they are uplifted to form mountains, followed by weathering and erosion. The sediments produced are transported, often to the sea, and deposited. Later they are buried by more sediment and become sedimentary rock.

The sedimentary rock may be uplifted again, as described above; alternatively, it may be buried more deeply, and deformed and recrystallised to form metamorphic rock.

Similarly, metamorphic rock may also be returned to the surface; if it is buried even more deeply it will melt and form magma and then either intrusive or extrusive igneous rock.

On the grand scale of the Earth, many rock cycle processes occur at plate boundaries, where plates are created or destroyed. For example, the increases in pressure and temperature needed to cause metamorphism in the crust occur in continental collision zones. Metamorphism also occurs in the crust at subduction zones, where rocks are dragged down to great depths and hence experience great pressures. Igneous processes take place wherever melting occurs in the mantle: beneath divergent plate boundaries, above the subducting plate at convergent plate boundaries, and far from plate boundaries at hot spots.

The sedimentary processes of erosion and deposition that are important elements of the rock cycle occur in a great variety of surface environments, such as glacial environments, deserts, and continental shelves. Great rivers, such as the Nile (North Africa) and the Mississippi (USA), transport sedimentary material many thousands of kilometres across plate interiors, laying down fertile muddy sediments and modifying the coastline by forming deltas. Other great rivers, such as the Ganges, Indus and Brahmaputra in India, rise in the high mountain belts where tectonic plates are colliding. In these collision zones, plate convergence thrusts mountains into the sky, but the steep mountain slopes and high rainfall encourage weathering and erosion. Consequently, the sites of mountain building generate prodigious amounts of sediment, which are washed away to be deposited elsewhere. For example, the Bay of Bengal contains several million cubic kilometres of sediment derived from the Himalayan Mountains. The fate of sediments is to be eroded and re-deposited or turned into sedimentary rocks. Those rocks can then be caught up in subduction zones, either entering the mantle, being forced onto the edge of a continental plate, or being trapped and metamorphosed in a continental collision.

Although the rock cycle moulds the geology of the crust, it does not operate in isolation. The weathering of rock is influenced by climatic effects. The transport and deposition of sediment varies according to the strength of water currents, wind speed or glacial action. The rock cycle is also greatly influenced by organisms. An obvious example is the formation of limestones from corals and other organisms, which form calcium carbonate skeletons or protective structures. Another way in which organisms affect the rock cycle is through weathering. Rocks are partly broken down by the physical action of wind and frost, and by the chemical decomposition of rainwater containing dissolved carbon dioxide, but this is greatly accelerated by plant roots, microorganisms, and other living organisms in the soil.

In Activity A 'Rocks and radioactivity', you will examine various rock samples and use your observations to deduce how the rocks formed (using the ideas in Sections 2.3 to 2.5). You will also place them in the context of the processes involved in the rock cycle.

2.9   Changing sea level

At the Residential School, as part of Activity C 'Investigating the environment', you will see sedimentary rocks that reveal how environmental conditions in Britain's geological past were extremely different from those of the present day (in fact 'Britain', like the rest of the Earth's geography, is transitory when viewed in terms of the very long span of geological time). As well as evidence from sedimentary rocks (using ideas similar to those introduced in Section 2.4), recent landforms also indicate that in the more recent geological past (in the Quaternary Period) sea level was not the same as it is today.

■   What deposits could you look for that might suggest sea level was once higher than at present?

☐   Beaches today are generally a mixture of pebbles or sand and shells and shell fragments. So, if you found such a deposit perched on a cliff above the present high-water mark, you could infer that, since it was deposited, sea level has fallen, leaving behind a **raised beach**.

Raised beaches, sometimes backed by an ancient cliff line, are common features around Britain's coast. Before explaining this observation, you need to know whether the sea level has fallen or the land has risen. Both are feasible: for instance, sea level can fall relative to a fixed land mass if the volume of the oceans shrinks because of cooling and the formation of land-based ice-caps. Similarly, it will rise if these ice caps melt. It so happens that since two to three million years ago the Earth has been in an ice age: a prolonged period of alternating glacial and interglacial periods characterised by the presence and absence of large polar ice caps. We are living in an interglacial period that was established about 10 000 years ago. As the volume of ice increases and decreases throughout an ice age, so the volume of the oceans decreases and increases. Some raised shorelines can therefore date from a previous interglacial period when the ocean volume was larger and, hence, sea level was higher than it is today.

However, nature is not quite so straightforward because the development and removal of thick ice sheets on land surfaces affects the elevation of the land, relative to sea level. In the last glacial period much of Britain was covered by an ice sheet up to 1.5 km thick for some 60 000 years. As this ice sheet melted, Britain was relieved of the enormous weight of the ice sheet, allowing the land to 'bounce back', like a ship rising out of the water when a heavy cargo is unloaded, with the result that the land moved relative to sea level, producing raised shorelines. A complex interplay of changing climate and Earth movements is therefore involved in producing many of the geologically recent coastal landforms of the British Isles. In addition, concerns about a rise in current sea level relate to yet a further process – rapid ocean warming accompanied by an expansion in the volume of seawater.

2.10   What to do next

You can check that you have understood the material in this chapter by working through the online interactive self-assessment questions for Chapter 2. You can access these questions via the link on the SXR103 course website.

You should now read through Sections 1 and 2 of the workbook for Activity C 'Investigating the environment', for the locations that you will visit during the Residential School. Section 1 outlines the guidelines for carrying out fieldwork and Section 2 introduces the geology of your field area.

2.11   Summary of Chapter 2

Rocks are classified into three types according to how they were formed. Igneous rocks are formed by crystallisation from the molten state; sedimentary rocks are deposited at the Earth's surface from water, air or ice; and metamorphic rocks are rocks of any origin that have been subsequently transformed (metamorphosed) by heat and/or pressure, often several kilometres below the Earth's surface.

Rocks are generally either crystalline (i.e. formed of interlocking mineral crystals), or fragmental (i.e. formed of mineral or rock fragments compacted and cemented together by later mineral growth). Most igneous and metamorphic rocks are crystalline, whereas most sedimentary rocks are fragmental. Most metamorphic rocks have foliation or mineral banding, which distinguishes them from igneous rocks. The presence of fossils usually indicates a sedimentary rock.

Slowly cooled magmas produce large crystals, whereas rapidly cooled magmas produce small crystals. The grain size of an igneous rock is therefore an indication of the cooling rate. Igneous rocks are classified according to grain size and the minerals present.

Metamorphic rocks may be produced around the margins of igneous intrusions (contact metamorphism) or throughout large volumes of rock in mountain-building events when continental plates collide (regional metamorphism). Regional metamorphism produces foliated or banded rocks, whose grain size increases with increasing pressure and temperature (depth).

The surface environment in which a sedimentary rock formed can be deduced from the character of the sedimentary grains and the types of any fossils and sedimentary structures present. For example: large grains indicate that the energy of the depositional environment was high; well-sorted, well-rounded grains indicate deposition from the air (wind transport); water-deposited sediments have poorer sorting and less rounded grains.

Rock exposures display the relationships between different rock types and the arrangement in space of those rocks. This gives additional information about how the exposed rocks were formed. The subsequent geological history can be deduced by identifying evidence for geological events that have altered earlier rocks (for example, folding will tilt originally horizontal beds, faulting will offset originally continuous beds, and a break in sedimentation will give an unconformity).

Sedimentary, metamorphic and igneous rocks are produced within a continuously operating cycle – the rock cycle – which is the path taken by the Earth's materials in response to chemical, biological and physical processes acting on rocks. The parts of the rock cycle that produce new sedimentary rocks involve weathering and erosion of pre-existing rocks, followed by transport and deposition of eroded mineral grains and rock fragments. Certain other sedimentary rocks are formed by biological processes, such as the accumulation of shells. In both cases, these processes occur on the Earth's surface. Most igneous and metamorphic rocks are produced near lithospheric plate boundaries.

The presence of raised beaches is evidence of a geologically recent change in sea level. The processes involved are a combination of climatically-influenced growth or melting of ice-caps and uplift of the land in response to unloading when ice sheets are removed by melting.

Now that you have completed Chapter 2 you should be able to:

- explain the difference between a mineral and a rock
- describe the textural differences between igneous, sedimentary and metamorphic rocks
- account for these differences in terms of the processes that produce these rocks
- classify igneous rocks according to their grain size and mineralogical composition
- recognise the difference between a body fossil and a trace fossil
- sketch a rock exposure and identify faults, folds and joints
- suggest a sequence of geological events that can best explain the features observed in a rock exposure
- relate processes of the rock cycle to a plate-tectonic setting
- describe the causes of sea-level changes and evidence for these changes
- understand how to use a hand lens.

Chapter 3
The physics of atoms, energy and radiation

3.1 Introduction

One of the fundamental questions that can be asked about our world is 'What is the nature of matter?' The notion that matter is made up of building blocks called **atoms** is an idea dating back to ancient Greece [Democritus, fifth century BCE], although scientific evidence for the existence of atoms is a much more recent development. Furthermore, it is only in the last 100 years or so that scientists have started to understand the properties of atoms in any detail.

Two of the experiments that you will do at the Residential School depend on the properties of atoms. In Activity B 'Analysing our environment', you will see that the electronic structure of atoms allows scientists to identify which types of atom might be present in a sample of material. In Activity A 'Rocks and radioactivity: energy in the Earth', you will find that an important source of energy within the Earth is the radioactive decay of nuclei of individual atoms.

3.2 The world's building blocks

An atom is a very small structure, about 10^{-10} m across (0.000 000 000 1 m). This is the main reason why it was historically so difficult to obtain direct evidence for the existence of atoms. However, with the benefit of modern techniques in microscopy, images of individual atoms can be formed (Figure 3.1). There are only about 100 or so different types of atom, which are termed the chemical **elements:** for example, hydrogen, oxygen, carbon and iron.

3.2.1 Atoms and electronic structure

At one time atoms were believed to be fundamental particles, i.e. they had no internal structure. It is now recognised that the atom is itself made up of smaller particles: **electrons**, **protons** and **neutrons**. Experiments carried out in the early twentieth century revealed that most of an atom's mass is concentrated in a central **nucleus**, which is now known to be made up of protons and neutrons. The nucleus is much smaller than the atom as a whole, being typically about 10^{-14} m across. We shall leave discussion of the nucleus and its interactions until Section 3.4.

The other component of atoms is a distribution of electrons surrounding the nucleus. This structure is shown schematically in Figure 3.2.

Electrons have much less mass than protons or neutrons, so they make only a tiny contribution to the mass of the atom. However, the behaviour of the electrons in an atom determines many of its characteristic properties. Indeed, the basis on which the science of chemistry is built is the idea that atoms combine together in a way that depends entirely on their electronic structures.

Figure 3.1 Surface map obtained with a scanning tunnelling microscope. Each blob represents an atom.

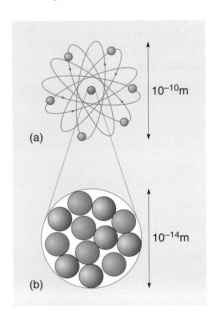

Figure 3.2 The constituents of a typical atom: (a) electrons move around the tiny nucleus, which is the core of the atom; (b) the nucleus is made up of particles called protons and neutrons.

One property of the atom that you will investigate in Activity B is its ability to emit light of very specific colours. As you will see in the next section, this phenomenon reveals much about the inner workings of atoms as well as being a very useful tool for identifying them.

Question 3.1

What fraction of the typical diameter of an atom is the diameter of its nucleus? Use the information in Sections 3.2 and 3.2.1, and express your answer in the form $1 \div$ (a number).

3.3   Spectral lines: an atom's signature

3.3.1 Spectra and spectral lines

When a beam of white light from the Sun is passed though a prism it is broken up, or dispersed, into a range of colours that form a pattern similar to a miniature rainbow. Such a band of colours is called a **spectrum** (plural spectra). The spectrum of white light from a conventional light bulb comprises an uninterrupted band of colours known as a **continuous spectrum**, an example of which is shown in Figure 3.3a. A similar technique can be used to study the light emitted by specific types of atom. An example of the type of source that can produce light in this way is a sodium street light. In this case, the spectrum is notably different from the continuous spectrum, as it consists of very narrow lines of specific colours (Figure 3.3b). This spectrum is termed an **emission spectrum** and the lines in it are called **spectral lines**. Sodium has very prominent yellow spectral lines as well as fainter green, red and blue lines.

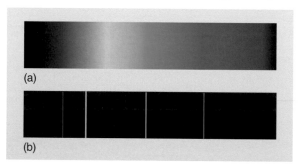

(a)

(b)

Figure 3.3   (a) A continuous spectrum from a beam of white light. (b) The emission spectrum of sodium.

How does this characteristic pattern of lines of different colours relate to the processes taking place within individual atoms? A starting point is to note that light carries energy from one place to another. A simple example of this is a 'solar-powered' calculator, in which the energy carried by light is converted into electrical energy. What is less obvious is that light carries energy in tiny 'packets'. These 'packets' are called quanta (singular **quantum**). In fact, there is a simple connection between the energy of quanta and the colour of light – quanta of red light have the lowest energy and quanta of violet light have the highest energy. When individual atoms produce light, they produce individual quanta. These 'packets' of light are often called **photons**.

One of the cornerstones of physics is the principle that energy is conserved. If, in an experiment to observe light from a particular type of atom you notice that photons of a certain energy (E_{ph}) are produced, this means that the atom itself must have lost exactly this amount of energy. In other words, there has been a change in the energy of the atom that is equal to the energy of the emitted photon. This can be expressed mathematically as:

$$\Delta E_{atom} = E_{ph} \tag{3.1}$$

where ΔE_{atom} is the change in the energy of the atom and E_{ph} is the energy of the photon. (The Greek letter Δ (delta) is often used in science to indicate a change in a quantity.)

The fact that atoms produce spectral lines of particular energies suggests something about the energy that atoms themselves can have, namely that they can have only specific energies. One way to visualise this is by means of a diagram that shows the **energy levels** that an atom can have. Figure 3.4 shows such a diagram for a hypothetical atom that has just two energy levels: a low energy level (E_{low}) and a high energy level (E_{high}). When the atom loses energy in the form of a photon, it makes a transition from the E_{high} to the E_{low} level. The energy of the photon is the difference between the two energy levels, i.e. $E_{ph} = E_{high} - E_{low}$. The opposite process can also occur. An atom that is in the E_{low} level can absorb a photon and reach the E_{high} level. However, only a photon with exactly the right amount of energy ($E_{high} - E_{low}$) can cause this transition.

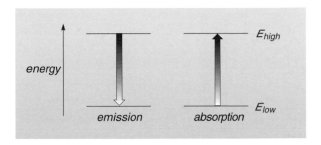

Figure 3.4   Changes in energy level for (left) an emission spectral line and (right) an absorption spectral line.

This two-state atom is much simpler than any real atom but the important feature is that this atom, like all real atoms, has discrete energy levels. Furthermore, each chemical element has its own distinctive pattern of energy levels. The energies of photons that are seen in the emission spectra of elements are determined by the spacings of these levels, so the spectrum is a unique 'signature' that can be used to identify that particular element.

■   A hypothetical atom has three energy levels – E_1, E_2 and E_3 – as shown in Figure 3.5. How many different transitions are possible that would result in the emission of photons? What are the energies of these photons?

☐   There are three possible transitions of this atom that will result in the emission of photons: $E_3 \longrightarrow E_1$, $E_3 \longrightarrow E_2$ and $E_2 \longrightarrow E_1$. These result in photons of energies ($E_3 - E_1$), ($E_3 - E_2$) and ($E_2 - E_1$), respectively.

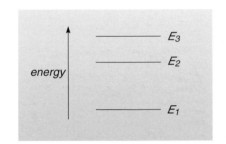

Figure 3.5   Energy-level diagram with three levels.

3.3.2 Discrete energy levels and spectra

You have seen that changes between discrete energy levels in an atom give rise to photons with particular energies, and that these photons form a characteristic spectrum. Spectra were first studied in the nineteenth century but, at that time, the origin of spectral lines was a mystery. Early in the twentieth century, physicists made considerable efforts to develop a model of the hydrogen atom because this is the simplest atom possible, having a single proton as the nucleus and a single electron. A key observation in understanding the interactions within an atom is the fact that both electrons and protons are electrically charged particles. All protons have a positive charge of the same value (which is called e). All electrons have a negative charge of $-e$. Two bodies with opposite charges will attract each other by an electric force. So a model of the hydrogen atom can be developed in which a negatively charged electron is bound by this electric force to the positively charged proton. This should give you a feel for how such a system might respond to changes in energy. Imagine a hypothetical atom in which the electron is initially close to the proton then, to transform this atom into a state in which the electron is more distant from the proton, work must be done to increase the separation of these two particles. So, in order to increase the separation of the electron from the proton, energy must be supplied to the atom. The converse is also true: when the separation of the electron and the proton decreases, energy is lost from the atom. This view of the atom explains how it can have different energies, but does not explain the fact that the atom can have only a discrete set of energy levels.

As a result of trying to solve this and other problems, a very successful, yet revolutionary, theory was developed in the first quarter of the twentieth century. This theory is called quantum mechanics, and it is remarkable because it requires many 'common-sense' notions about how particles behave to be discarded. It is not necessary to delve into the quantum origins of the discrete energy levels in atoms in order to use spectra for scientific purposes, and we shall not do so here. You should simply accept that atoms do have discrete energy levels.

It is useful to look at the energy-level diagram that the quantum mechanical model of the hydrogen atom predicts to see how it relates to the observed spectrum of hydrogen. The energy level diagram is shown in Figure 3.6a. The first point to note about this diagram is that there is a minimum energy that the atom can have. This is called the **ground state** of the atom and it corresponds to a state where the average distance between the electron and the proton has the smallest value of any energy level. This energy level is labelled '$n = 1$', where n is the principal **quantum number**. At higher energies than the ground state there are **excited states**, labelled $n = 2, 3, 4$, and so on, which correspond to increases in the average separation of the electron and proton. Note that the energy levels are not evenly separated: in fact, as n increases, the energy difference between successive levels gets progressively smaller, until an energy is reached at which the electron is free from the influence of the proton. It is important to realise that even though the energy level spacings get smaller, the average separation increases dramatically so that, at a high enough energy, the electron is no longer a part of the atom. The process of removing an electron from an atom is called **ionisation**, and an atom that has lost one (or more) electrons so that it is no longer electrically neutral is called an **ion**.

An atom emits a photon when the atom makes a transition from one energy state to a lower energy state. For instance, if the hydrogen atom changes from the $n = 3$ to the $n = 2$ state, a photon is emitted that corresponds to a red line in the spectrum. The transition from the $n = 4$ state to the $n = 2$ state results in a photon of higher energy, because the energy difference between the $n = 4$ level and the $n = 2$ level is greater than the energy difference between the $n = 3$ level and the $n = 2$ level. The transition from the $n = 4$ state to the $n = 2$ state results in a spectral line that is in the blue part of the spectrum. For the transition from the $n = 5$ state to the $n = 2$ state, a photon of yet higher energy is emitted, in this case corresponding to a violet spectral line. This

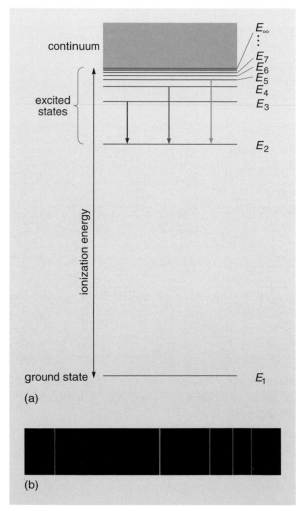

Figure 3.6   (a) The energy-level diagram of hydrogen. (b) The visible part of the emission spectrum of hydrogen.

trend continues, and as Figure 3.6b shows, there is a distinctive pattern of lines at particular energies that correspond to transitions to the $n = 2$ state.

You might be wondering about where in the spectrum a line from a transition to the $n = 1$ level might appear. The lowest energy photon from such a transition arises from a change from the $n = 2$ state to the $n = 1$ state. This corresponds to a photon that is more energetic than a photon of violet light, and so it lies in the ultraviolet part of the spectrum. The human eye cannot see this part of the spectrum. Similarly, transitions between closely separated levels give rise to photons with less energy than photons of red light, and these photons lie in the infrared part of the spectrum, so again humans cannot see them.

In summary, an atom that is above its ground state produces photons of energies that reflect the separation between energy levels in that atom. Here we have concentrated on the spectrum produced by hydrogen atoms. Other chemical elements have energy level diagrams that are different from that of hydrogen, and there is a unique and distinguishing spectrum for each element.

3.3.3 The production of emission spectra

To make an atom produce photons, the atom must be raised above its ground state, which is done by supplying energy to the atom. One way of doing this is the opposite of the emission process that described above. You have seen that when an atom loses energy it does so by emitting photons with energies that correspond to the differences between energy levels. In the opposite process, an atom in one energy state can transform to another higher energy state by absorbing a photon. However, the incoming photon must have an energy that corresponds to the difference between the two energy levels for this to occur. Another method of raising energy states is to make atoms collide. In this case, some of the energy of the collision may be absorbed by one of the atoms, causing it to change to a higher energy state. In practice, this can be achieved readily by heating a gaseous sample containing the atoms that are being studied. This can be done by introducing a sample into a flame. Figure 3.7 shows an example of a flame test. Here, an experimenter places a small amount of sample on a platinum wire, and moves it into a hot flame. The colour of the flame – a mixture of the spectral lines produced by the elements in the sample – helps to identify those elements. In Activity B 'Analysing our environment', gas burners are used to produce flames containing samples of metal ions that you will be asked to identify.

Figure 3.7 A flame test. In this case, the bluish-green colour of the flame indicates the presence of copper.

■ Figure 3.7 shows an experimenter doing a flame test experiment. He has failed to take a fundamental safety precaution. What is this precaution and what are the reasons for it?

☐ The experimenter should be wearing a laboratory coat to protect him and his clothing, and to protect the experiment he is working on from outside contamination. Since you must take off your laboratory coat before leaving the laboratory, this also prevents you carrying contamination outside. For further safety information, see Section 1.3.

3.3.4 Spectroscopy: measuring spectral signatures

The technique of identifying which metal atoms are present in a sample of material by analysing the spectrum of emitted photons is called **spectroscopy**. Scientists often want to discover which elements may be present in a sample of material, and spectroscopy provides the means to this end in a wide range of applications, e.g. analysing drinking water and investigating the composition of stars. In Activity B you will identify elements from their spectra. The next section describes some of the theory behind the technique of spectroscopy that you need to know before starting the practical work.

3.3.5 Energies and wavelengths

You have already seen that elements have a **spectral signature** that consists of spectral lines at characteristic energies. In practice it is rather difficult to measure the energies of photons directly, but there is an indirect way of measuring photon energy that relies on the fact that light behaves like a wave.

If you have ever spent any time at the seaside you are probably aware of the most important features of waves. A **wave** is a periodic or repeating disturbance that carries energy from one place to another. A typical profile of the disturbance caused by a wave on water is shown in Figure 3.8. One characteristic of a wave is the distance between two consecutive peaks (or troughs). This is called the **wavelength** and is usually denoted by λ (the Greek letter lambda). In the case of light, the wavelength is a very short distance, only about 4×10^{-7} m or so, which is one reason why the wave-like nature of light is not obvious to humans.

Figure 3.8 Diagram of wavelength.

The exact nature of light need not concern you too much here, but it is useful to know that light is one example of a phenomenon called **electromagnetic radiation**. The wavelengths of electromagnetic waves cover an enormous range: from over 10^4 m for radio waves to less than 10^{-16} m for **gamma rays**. (You will meet gamma rays again in Section 3.5 when energy changes in the nucleus of an atom are discussed.)

The wavelength of all electromagnetic radiation has a simple relationship with the energy carried by its photons. This relationship can be written mathematically as:

$$E_{\text{ph}} = \frac{hc}{\lambda} \tag{3.2}$$

where h is a quantity called the Planck constant (named after the German physicist Max Planck) and c is the speed of light in a vacuum.

■ Both h and c are constants. According to Equation 3.2, what determines the energy of a photon?

☐ The energy of a photon is determined by the wavelength of the light (λ).

You can also see from Equation 3.2 that, if the wavelength is very large, the photon energy is very small and vice versa. You have seen that atoms produce spectral lines of given energies but you could equally well say that the atom produces spectral lines at particular wavelengths.

■ Yellow light comprises photons of lower energy than the photons comprising green light. Which colour has the longer wavelength?

☐ Equation 3.2 shows that energy decreases as wavelength increases. So, if yellow light has lower energy photons than green light, yellow light must have a longer wavelength than green light.

3.3.6 Measuring the wavelength of spectral lines

The wavelengths of spectral lines can be measured by generating spectra so that the position of a line in the spectrum can be related to its wavelength. Using a prism to form such a spectrum is not very well suited to this task. However, there is a different type of optical device, called a **diffraction grating**, which produces a spectrum in which the position in the observed spectrum can easily be related to wavelength. A diffraction grating is simply a series of very narrow, evenly spaced slits. To form the spectrum, the grating is set up so that the light being analysed hits the grating at an angle of 90°, as shown in Figure 3.9.

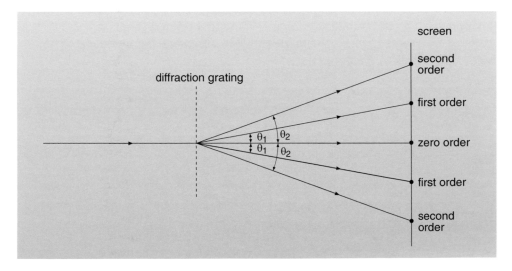

Figure 3.9   The pattern formed by a diffraction grating.

The grating makes light of a given wavelength form more than one beam after it has passed through the grating, forming what is called a diffraction pattern. Consider what happens if light of a single wavelength (or **monochromatic** light) is shone on the diffraction grating. Some light passes straight through the grating; this is called the zero order beam. Another beam is produced that is an angle, θ_1, from the straight through position. This is called first order diffraction, and an identical beam is produced at an angle, θ_1, in the other direction from the straight through position. The importance of this diffracted beam is that the angle the beam emerges at (the **angle of diffraction**) is related to the wavelength, λ, of the light by the equation:

$$\sin \theta_1 = \frac{\lambda}{d} \qquad (3.3)$$

where d is the **grating spacing**, the distance between the centres of two adjacent slits on the grating. This means if the value of d for the grating is known then, assuming that the angle of diffraction can be measured, the wavelength of the light can be calculated. (See Appendix 1 if you need a reminder about the use of sines.)

The diffraction pattern includes other beams of light of this wavelength. At an even higher angle from the straight through position there will be a second diffracted beam, which is called the second order diffraction. In this case too, there is a simple mathematical relationship between the angle of diffraction, which is now called θ_n and the wavelength:

$$\sin \theta_n = \frac{n\lambda}{d} \qquad (3.4)$$

The quantity n is called the **order of diffraction**. For first order diffraction $n = 1$ and for second order diffraction $n = 2$. It is possible to generate third ($n = 3$) and higher orders of diffraction, but you will not do this in Activity B.

Question 3.2

A beam of light is diffracted by a grating that has a spacing of 1.667×10^{-6} m. The spectrum produced by the grating has one first order diffraction beam at an angle of 19.8° and another at an angle of 23.4°. Calculate the wavelengths of both components of the light.

3.3.7 Getting to know the spectrometer

In Activity B you will use an instrument called a **spectrometer** to study the diffracted beams of light from a diffraction grating. Figure 3.10 shows a plan view of a spectrometer.

The spectrometer consists of a table on which the diffraction grating is mounted. The light to be analysed passes through an instrument called a **collimator** before striking the diffraction grating at an angle of 90°.

Before striking the grating, the beam of light should not be spreading out or getting narrower; this is called a parallel beam. The collimator contains a series of lenses which, when properly focused, will produce a parallel beam. In addition to being a parallel beam, it is a great advantage if the light to be analysed is in a narrow beam. This is because the diffracted beams are the same width as the incoming beam, and the narrower the diffracted beam, the more precisely the angle of diffraction can be measured.

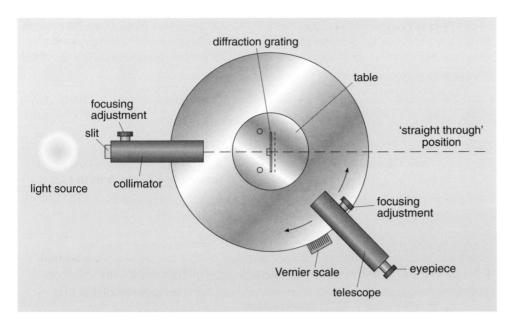

Figure 3.10   Schematic diagram of a spectrometer.

After passing through the grating, light is diffracted into beams that emerge at angles depending on the wavelength of the line. These emergent diffracted beams are seen through a **telescope**, which can be rotated around the table. An angular scale that runs around the table allows the position of the telescope to be determined for any observed beam.

3.3.8 Spectroscopy in Activity B

There is a full description of Activity B in the workbook, but the main stages dealing with spectroscopy are as follows. The overall aim is to identify metals by investigating the visible light they emit when heated to high temperatures.

The first part of the activity is a visual investigation of the colours of flames of unknown samples (see Figure 3.7). This analysis is then taken further by observing the spectra of these flames with a handheld **spectroscope** (a device which produces a spectrum but cannot easily be used to measure the wavelength of any spectral lines). The activity then moves on to using a spectrometer of the type described in the previous section. Before the spectrometer can be used, the collimator and the telescope need to be properly focused, and the spectrometer needs to be **calibrated**. The aim of the calibration process is to determine the value of the grating spacing, d, of the particular grating that you will be given. This involves using a spectral line as a wavelength standard and, for this activity, a bright yellow spectral line of sodium is used. Finally, the calibrated spectrometer is used to measure the wavelengths of spectral lines obtained from flames containing unknown metals. These metals can then be identified from the pattern of observed spectral lines.

Table 3.1 Angles of diffraction (for use in Task 1).

n	$\theta_n/°$	$\sin \theta_n$
0	0.0	
1	12.1	
2	25.1	
3	39.2	
4	57.5	

You should now read about the investigation in more detail in Part B of the Activity B workbook. To conclude this introduction to spectroscopy, you should complete Activity 3.1, in which you will analyse spectrometer data with the aim of calibrating an instrument.

Activity 3.1   Calibrating a diffraction grating

Suggested study time: 90 minutes

The aim of this data analysis activity is to find a value for the grating spacing, d, of a diffraction grating from some data which we will give you. This activity should also give you confidence in plotting and using graphs. It is divided into several distinct tasks. If you have any doubts about the way in which you have answered the questions related to these tasks, you should compare your answers with those given at the end of this book.

Before using the spectrometer to measure the wavelength of spectral lines, it is calibrated using a monochromatic source that produces light at a known, fixed wavelength of 632.8 nm. (The **nanometre**, symbol nm, equals 10^{-9} m and is a unit used frequently when discussing the wavelength of light.) Diffracted beams are observed up to and including the fourth order. The angles of diffraction are shown in Table 3.1.

Task 1 (30 minutes)

Starting with the diffraction equation below, answer the questions following it.

$$\sin \theta_n = \frac{n\lambda}{d} \tag{3.4}$$

(a) Which terms in Equation 3.4 are: (i) known, (ii) unknown or (iii) measured in the experiment?
(b) Does Equation 3.4 describe a straight-line relationship between the two measured quantities in the experiment? If not, how can a straight-line relationship be obtained? (**Hint:** remember that a straight-line graph going through the origin can be described by an equation of the form $y = kx$, where x and y are the variables plotted on the graph, and k is a constant. Appendix 2 has more details about the equations of straight-line graphs.)
(c) Suppose that you plot a graph of $\sin \theta_n$ against n. How would you find the value of d (the spacing of the grating) from such a graph?

Task 2 (20 minutes)

Now you will calculate the quantities that are needed to plot the required graph. Complete the blank column in Table 3.1 by calculating the sines of the angles of diffraction.

Task 3 (40 minutes)

Now you need to plot the straight line, measure its gradient and calculate d.
(a) On the graph paper in Figure 3.11, plot a graph of $\sin \theta_n$ (vertical axis) against n (horizontal axis). Draw a straight line that is the best fit to the data on this graph.
(b) Now find the gradient of the best-fit line.
(c) Calculate a value for d. Express your answer in nanometres and in metres.

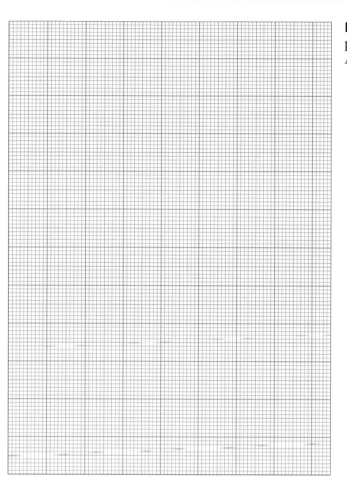

Figure 3.11   Graph paper for use in Activity 3.1.

For the answers to this activity refer to the section at the end of this book.

3.4   Into the nucleus

This chapter has already discussed the fact that atomic nuclei contain protons and neutrons. Each proton carries a positive charge exactly equal in size to the negative charge carried by an electron and, as the name suggests, neutrons are electrically neutral. This implies that each electrically neutral atom must contain the same number of protons as electrons. It is this number (called the **atomic number**, Z) that determines an element's chemical properties: if the number of protons in an atom is altered, it becomes an atom of a different element. For example, hydrogen atoms always contain one proton, copper atoms always contain 29 protons, and gold atoms always contain 79 protons.

The neutrons inside a nucleus do not contribute to its charge, but they do contribute to its mass. Some elements exist in several different forms, called **isotopes**, each with the same atomic number (i.e. the same number of protons), but with different numbers of neutrons and hence different masses. For example, there are three naturally occurring isotopes of uranium; all three have 92 protons (this number identifies the element as uranium), but one has 142 neutrons, one has 143 neutrons and one has 146 neutrons. The total number of neutrons

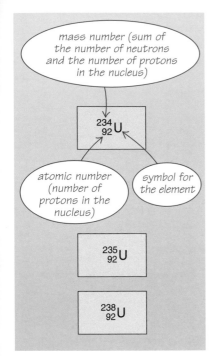

Figure 3.12 Symbolic representations of the three isotopes of uranium. Note that the atomic number (and hence the number of protons) is the same for each one, indicating that they are the same element; but the mass number is different, indicating that they are different isotopes.

and protons (known collectively as **nucleons**) in a nucleus defines its **mass number**, A. Thus the mass numbers of the three naturally occurring isotopes of uranium are 234 (92 protons plus 142 neutrons), 235 (92 protons and 143 neutrons) and 238 (92 protons and 146 neutrons) respectively. The isotopes are commonly referred to as uranium-234, uranium-235 and uranium-238.

Sometimes it is useful to represent atoms by symbols that show both the mass number and the atomic number, and hence the number of protons and neutrons in the nucleus. Against the symbol for the element, the atomic number is written as a preceding subscript, and the mass number as a preceding superscript. The helium atom has an atomic number of 2 and a mass number of 4, so it is written as $^{4}_{2}\text{He}$.

■   How many protons and neutrons are there in the helium atom?

☐   The atomic number is 2, so there are two protons.

The mass number gives the number of protons plus neutrons, so the number of neutrons is the mass number minus the atomic number $= 4 - 2 = 2$.

Figure 3.12 shows the symbolic representation for the three isotopes of uranium considered above.

3.5   Radioactive decay

In Activity A, 'Rocks and radioactivity' you will investigate **radioactive decay**, the process whereby certain unstable atomic nuclei break up or decay spontaneously, with the release of energy. There are various types of decay but the three most important ones in this activity are those called **alpha-decay** (**α-decay**), **beta-minus-decay** (**β⁻-decay**) and **gamma-decay** (**γ-decay**).

3.5.1   Alpha-decay

An example of an α-decay process is:

$$^{234}_{92}\text{U} \longrightarrow {}^{230}_{90}\text{Th} + {}^{4}_{2}\text{He} + \text{energy}$$

In words, a uranium (U) nucleus (the parent nucleus) decays to produce a thorium (Th) nucleus (the daughter nucleus), a helium nucleus and energy. The helium nucleus is more commonly known as an **alpha-particle** (**α-particle**). Note that the number of protons in the product is not the same as that in the parent nucleus, so the product is no longer uranium, but an isotope of thorium. Notice too that the overall mass number and the total charge are the same on both sides of the equation: the mass number on the left (234) is equal to the sum of the mass numbers on the right (230 + 4); the charge on the nucleus on the left (from 92 protons in the uranium nucleus) is equal to the total charge on the nuclei on the right (from 90 protons in the thorium nucleus and two protons in the α-particle). Equations representing nuclear decays must always balance, i.e.:

•   Electric charge is always conserved: the net charge on the products of a nuclear decay is the same as the net charge of the original nucleus.

•   The mass number is conserved: the total number of nucleons in the products is the same as that in the original nucleus.

3.5.2 Where does the energy come from?

You should be familiar with the idea that energy is conserved in all physical processes. So where does the 'energy' on the right-hand side of the equation come from? The answer lies in Einstein's famous equation, $E = mc^2$. Accurate measurements of the masses of the α-particle and the thorium nucleus reveal that their sum is *less* than the mass of the original uranium nucleus by about 8.66×10^{-30} kg, an infinitesimally small amount. This mass is converted into energy during the decay. Taking a value for c, the speed of light – of 3.00×10^8 ms^{-1} – tells you that this lost mass is equivalent to an energy of:

$$E = mc^2 = 8.66 \times 10^{-30} \text{ kg} \times (3.00 \times 10^8 \text{ m s}^{-1})^2 = 7.79 \times 10^{-13} \text{ J}$$

Thus the α-decay of one atom of $^{234}_{92}U$ liberates 7.79×10^{-13} J of energy. This is almost exclusively carried away as kinetic energy by the α-particle. Note that the amount of energy released per atom is very small. Another unit for energy, MeV (the megaelectronvolt, where 1 MeV $= 1.6 \times 10^{-13}$ J), is sometimes used, but for simplicity only the joule is used here.

3.5.3 Beta-minus-decay

An example of a β⁻-decay process is:

$$^{137}_{55}\text{Cs} \longrightarrow {}^{137}_{56}\text{Ba} + e^- + \overline{v}_e + \text{energy}$$

In words, a caesium (CS) nucleus decays to produce a barium (Ba) nucleus, a high energy electron, another particle called an **electron antineutrino** ($\overline{v}_e$) and energy. The antineutrino has no charge, negligible mass and is very difficult to detect. The electron given off in the process was not initially recognised as an electron, so it became known as a **beta-particle (β-particle)**.

First, check that the equation balances. The electron carries a negative charge exactly equal in size to the positive charge carried by a proton, and the antineutrino has no charge. Thus the charge on the left-hand side (from the 55 protons in the caesium nucleus) is equal to the charge on the right-hand side (from the 56 protons in the barium nucleus and the single negatively charged electron). Also, both sides have a mass number of 137. But where has the electron come from? This is a *nuclear* decay, so it has not come from the electrons surrounding the nucleus in the atom. Neither was it in the nucleus in the first place – nuclei don't contain electrons! The correct explanation involves noting that, since the barium nucleus contains one more proton than the caesium nucleus, but the same number of nucleons altogether, it must contain one less neutron than the original caesium nucleus. What has happened is that one of the neutrons in the caesium nucleus has been transformed into a proton, with the emission of an electron and an antineutrino.

3.5.4 Gamma-decay

In contrast to the processes of α- and β⁻-decay, γ-decay involves no change in the numbers of neutrons and protons. Instead it occurs in a process which is analogous to the one giving rise to *atomic* spectra (see Section 3.3.2 and Figure 3.6a). Gamma-decay occurs when a *nucleus* makes a transition from a state of high energy to one of lower energy, and the transition is accompanied by the emission of a photon, for example:

$$^{137}_{56}\text{Ba (excited state)} \longrightarrow {}^{137}_{56}\text{Ba (ground state)} + \gamma$$

The photon emitted in the nuclear process has an energy around one million times larger than in the atomic one, so it is a γ-ray photon rather than a photon of visible light. Excited states of nuclei may be created as a result of α-decay or β⁻-decay, so γ-decay often accompanies other types of radioactive decay.

Activity 3.2   The decay of uranium

Suggested study time: 30 minutes

In this activity you will look in more detail at the decay of $^{238}_{92}$U. More than 99% of the uranium in the Earth is present as this radioactive isotope. Table 3.2 shows a partially completed decay scheme for it. As you can see, $^{238}_{92}$U does not decay straight to a stable product but through a variety of decay processes, each of which gives an intermediate radioactive isotope, until it eventually decays to give a stable isotope of lead (Pb). Many of the daughter nuclides produced in this decay are created in excited states and decay by γ-ray emission to their ground state before a subsequent α- or β⁻-decay occurs, but the γ-ray emissions are not shown in Table 3.2.

Table 3.2 Radioactive decay scheme for uranium-238.

Step	Parent	Decay	Daughter
1	$^{238}_{92}$U	α	$^{234}_{90}$Th
2	$^{234}_{90}$Th	β⁻	$^{234}_{91}$Pa
3	$^{234}_{91}$Pa	β⁻	$^{234}_{92}$U
4	$^{234}_{92}$U	α	$^{230}_{90}$Th
5	$^{230}_{90}$Th		$^{226}_{88}$Ra
6	$^{226}_{88}$Ra		$^{222}_{86}$Rn
7	$^{222}_{86}$Rn		$^{218}_{84}$Po
8	$^{218}_{84}$Po		$^{214}_{82}$Pb
9	$^{214}_{82}$Pb		$^{214}_{83}$Bi
10	$^{214}_{83}$Bi		$^{214}_{84}$Po
11	$^{214}_{84}$Po		$^{210}_{82}$Pb
12	$^{210}_{82}$Pb		$^{210}_{83}$Bi
13	$^{210}_{83}$Bi		$^{210}_{84}$Po
14	$^{210}_{84}$Po		$^{206}_{82}$Pb (stable)

Task 1 (15 minutes)

Each step in the decay scheme in Table 3.2 is either an α-decay or a β⁻-decay. Use the rules you have learned about the conservation of charge and mass number to work out which type of decay leads to each product and thus complete Table 3.2.

Task 2 (15 minutes)

Each time a single $^{238}_{92}U$ nucleus decays to $^{206}_{82}Pb$ by way of the decay scheme in Table 3.2, a total mass of about 9.2×10^{-29} kg is lost. Use the equation $E = mc^2$ to calculate the corresponding energy (in joules).

For the answers to this activity refer to the section at the end of this book.

3.5.5 When do nuclei decay?

Some isotopes are stable and others are unstable; the unstable nuclei are those that decay. But when will this decay happen? The simple answer is that we don't know. Radioactive decay is an intrinsically random process and we can never know when an individual nucleus will decay. However, for a large enough number of nuclei, the concept of **half-life** (i.e. the time taken for half of a radioactive sample to decay) can be used as a measure of how rapidly the isotope is likely to decay. Half-life is a useful and important concept because it gives an indication of the persistence of a radioactive isotope in the environment. For some uses, for example in medicine, isotopes with a short half-life are required: the half-life of technetium-99 (which is used as a radioactive tracer in the body) is about 6 hours. In contrast, isotopes used in radioactive dating need to have a relatively long half-life (the half-life of carbon-14 is 5700 years) but sometimes even that is not long enough (the half-life of uranium-238 is 4.5×10^9 years).

An analogy may help you to understand the random nature of radioactive decay and the concept of half-life. If you take a coin and toss it, the probability of getting 'heads' is 1 in 2, i.e. each time you toss the coin you have a 50 : 50 chance of this outcome. You have absolutely no way of knowing whether you will get 'heads' or 'tails' on the next throw (in fact, it is possible to toss the coin 100 times and get 'tails' every time) but, if you do an enormous of throws you will get heads about half of the time. Now imagine that, instead of tossing a coin, you throw a die ('die' is the singular of 'dice'). There are more options available than there were for the coin (six possible scores as opposed to just two – heads and tails), so each possible outcome (e.g. throwing a six) is less likely. So, although you never know whether a particular toss of a coin or throw of a die is going to produce heads or a six, it seems reasonable to suppose that a model of radioactive decay based on scoring a six when you throw a die will somehow be a slower process than a similar model based on getting heads when you throw a coin. You will investigate this further in the next activity.

Activity 3.3 Tossing coins and throwing dice

Suggested study time: 60 minutes

We gave a group of students a tub containing 100 coins and asked them to do the following experiment.

1 Throw all the coins out of the tub onto a table (this represents 'throw number 1' as indicated in Table 3.3).

2 Collect all the heads and count them, and *put these coins to one side*. These coins represent the number of atoms that decayed in the first time interval.

3 Return the other ('non-decayed') coins to the tub and throw again ('throw number 2' as indicated in Table 3.3).

4 Again collect heads, count them and put these coins to one side.

5 Repeat steps 3 and 4 until all the coins have been put to one side.

A total of 46 heads were collected on the first throw, 20 on the second, 17 on the third, and so on. This simulation was labelled 'run A' and the students then repeated the whole simulation a further nine times (runs B to J), and added the results together, so it was as if they had started with 1000 coins. Figure 3.13 shows the experiment in progress and the results are given in Table 3.3.

(a)

(b)

(c)

Figure 3.13 Simulating radioactive decay using coins. (a) The coins are thrown out of the tub. (b) Heads ('decayed atoms') are counted and put to one side. (c) The other ('non-decayed') coins are returned to the tub.

Table 3.3 Results of a simulation of radioactive decay using coins.

Throw number	Number of heads thrown in run:										Total for runs A–J
	A	**B**	**C**	**D**	**E**	**F**	**G**	**H**	**I**	**J**	
1	46	50	55	51	43	53	54	53	58	48	511
2	20	24	19	20	26	33	23	27	25	32	249
3	17	14	9	15	21	2	8	11	5	8	110
4	8	6	9	7	8	6	7	6	6	8	71
5	5	3	5	1	0	4	6	3	2	2	31
6	3	2	3	4	1	1	2	–	0	2	18
7	0	1	–	1	1	0	–	–	4	–	7
8	0	–	–	0	–	1	–	–	–	–	1
9	0	–	–	1	–	–	–	–	–	–	1
10	0	–	–	–	–	–	–	–	–	–	0
11	1	–	–	–	–	–	–	–	–	–	1

Task 1 (20 minutes)

Plot points on the graph paper in Figure 3.14 to show the total number of heads collected at each throw against the throw number. The axes are labelled and the first two points are plotted to help you.

Task 2 (5 minutes)

Draw the 'best-fit' curve on Figure 3.14. Your points will not lie exactly on a smooth curve, but your best-fit curve should be a smooth curve that is as close as possible to as many of the points as possible.

Task 3 (35 minutes)

(a) Use your graph to find the number of throws required to halve the 'number of heads thrown'. This represents the half-life of the process. Note that half-life does not depend on the actual number of coins (or atoms) decaying. You should get a similar result by considering, for example, the interval between 400 heads thrown and 200 heads thrown as you would get by considering the interval between 200 heads thrown and 100 heads thrown; the important point is that the number of heads thrown is halved. Find three values for the half-life of the process from your graph, and then find their mean.

(b) Is the result what you expected or not?

(c) How would you expect a graph drawn for a very large set of data (say 10 000 coins to start with) to compare with the one you have drawn?

(d) Figure 3.15 shows the results from a different simulation of radioactive decay; this time an idealised representation of throwing 1000 dice. The dice are considered to have 'decayed' when a six is thrown. How do the graph in Figure 3.15 and the value of the half-life for the process it represents compare with the graph you plotted for coins in Tasks 1 and 2 and the half-life that you found in Task 3a?

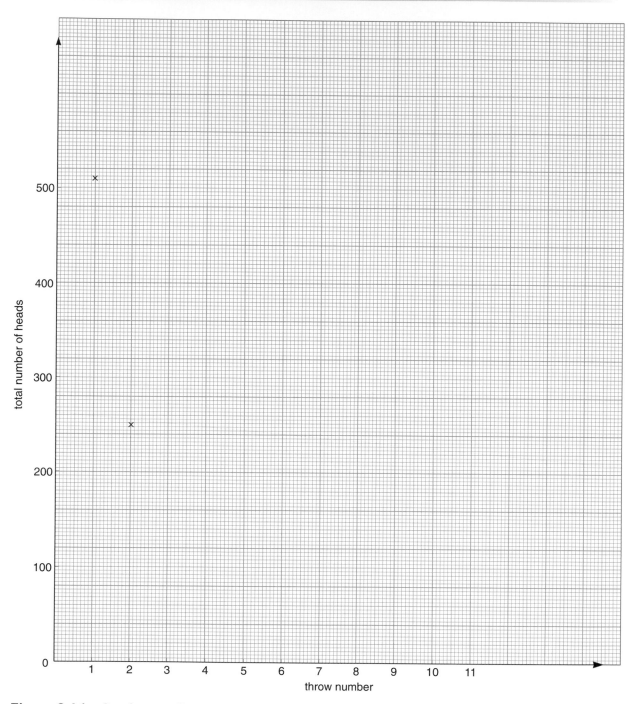

Figure 3.14   Graph paper for use in Activity 3.3.

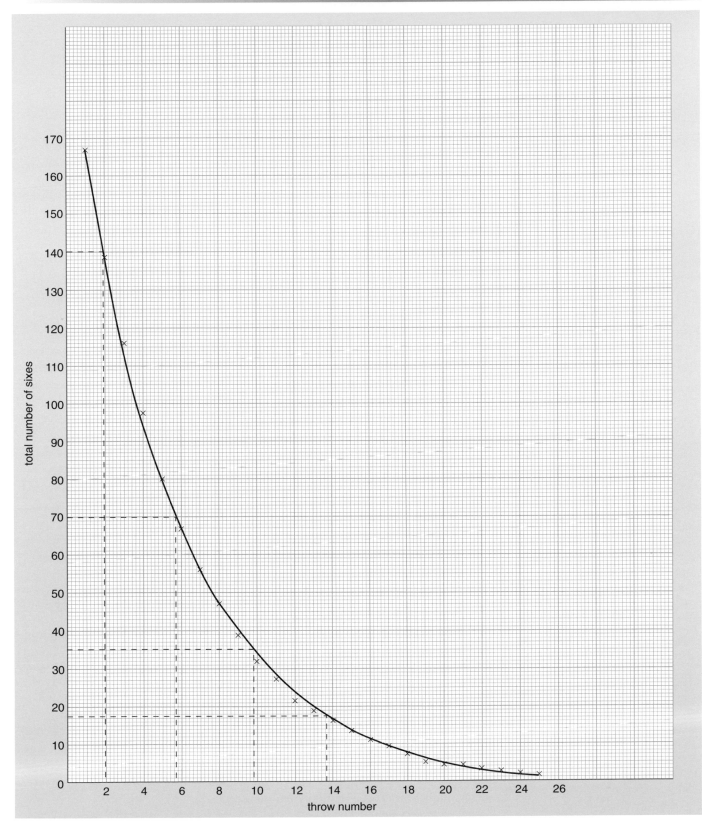

Figure 3.15   Total number of sixes thrown at each throw number.

For the answers to this activity refer to the section at the end of this book.

3.5.6 'Counting' radioactivity

In Activity A you will use several different radioactive sources and 'count' the radioactivity they produce with a **Geiger counter** like that shown in Figure 3.16. The cap has been removed from the end of the Geiger tube so that you can see the entrance window through which radiation passes. When an α-particle, an electron or a γ-ray photon enters the Geiger tube, it creates an electrical signal that is recorded by the attached counter. The digital display on the counter records the number of radioactive 'particles' that have been detected. The counter can also be set up to 'click' every time a particle is detected.

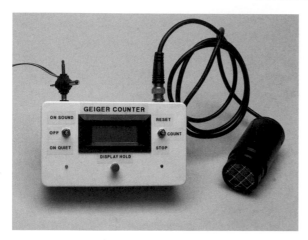

Figure 3.16   A Geiger counter, consisting of a tube connected to a meter that displays the measurements.

3.5.7 Counting statistics and uncertainties

If you look back to Table 3.3 you will see that there was considerable variation between the results of the different runs in the tossing coins simulation: for example, in run C, 55 heads were collected for the first throw whereas in run E only 43 heads were collected for the first throw. This is because the process is governed by probability, so you can never know how many heads are going to be thrown. However, as more and more coins are tossed, the overall ratio of heads to tails gets closer and closer to the theoretical 50 : 50. A similar situation applies every time you use a Geiger counter to 'count' radioactive decays. If you use the same Geiger counter at a fixed distance from a fixed source to take the five consecutive readings for the count in the same period of time, your readings are likely to be different. However, if you could repeat the measurement, say, 1000 times, a pattern would begin to emerge. Figure 3.17a shows a histogram of 1000 such measurements, plotted as the 'number of times there were the given number of decays in one minute' against the 'number of decays in one minute'. As you can see, there is a most probable value for the number of decays, which in this case is about 100 decays in one minute.

The overall shape of the histogram in Figure 3.17a can be approximated by a well-known mathematical curve which is drawn in Figure 3.17b. Don't worry too much about the detail of Figure 3.17, or the following two paragraphs of text. The important point is that you know how to calculate the uncertainty in a count rate; not that you understand the underlying theory.

The curve shown in Figure 3.17b has two useful properties. First, the position of the peak of the distribution corresponds to the mean value, m, of all the measurements: the mean value is therefore also the most probable value. Second, 68% of all the measurements lie within $\sqrt{m}$ either side of this mean ($\sqrt{m}$ means the square root of m, i.e. the number which, if squared – multiplied by itself – would give m. For example, $3 \times 3 = 9$, so the square root of $9 = 3$). So there is a 68% probability that any individual measurement will lie within ($\sqrt{m}$) of the most probable value of m, i.e. $m \pm \sqrt{m}$. For the results shown in Figure 3.17a, since the square root of 100 is 10, this means that 68% of the measurements lie between $(100 - 10) = 90$ and $(100 + 10) = 110$ decays in one minute, or 100 ± 10.

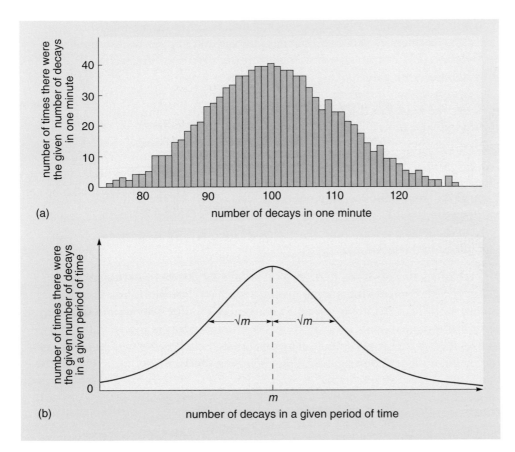

(a)

number of decays in one minute

(b)

number of decays in a given period of time

Figure 3.17   (a) Histogram showing the results of repeating a background count measurement 1000 times. (b) The mathematical curve to which the histogram may be approximated.

Now, suppose you don't have the time (or patience!) to take 1000 measurements, but you take *just one* measurement with a value *n*, say. There is a 68% probability that the single measurement you have taken lies within $\sqrt{m}$ either side of the mean value *m* that you would get if you took 1000 measurements. You don't know what this mean value is (you only have the one measurement), but the argument can be turned around to say that there is a 68% probability that the mean value of a thousand measurements would lie within $\sqrt{n}$ of the single measurement with value *n*.

This will save you a lot of time! Rather than taking 1000 measurements, just take one measurement with a value *n* and then assume that there is a 68% probability that the mean value of 1000 measurements would lie somewhere within the range covered by $n \pm \sqrt{n}$. Although 68% may not seem like a very high probability, it is perfectly acceptable in practice. The 'plus or minus the square root of *n*' is referred to as the **uncertainty** of the particular value *n* that you have measured. In general, any radioactive count that you record with a Geiger counter should be expressed in the form of the number *n* with its associated uncertainty, given by $\pm \sqrt{n}$.

■   Suppose you use a Geiger counter to obtain a count rate of 57 counts per minute. Give this count rate with its associated uncertainty (round up the uncertainty to the whole number above it).

☐ $\sqrt{57} = 7.55 = 8$ to the whole number above, so the count rate per minute is 57 ± 8.

You will need to think about experimental uncertainties frequently when you are at the Residential School. In general, the uncertainty in a measurement is an estimate of its true range. We have already discussed the need to give uncertainties with your readings for count rate in Activity A. In Activity B, 'Analysing our environment', you will discover that it is only possible to measure the angles of diffraction on your spectrometer to the nearest 0.1°, so the uncertainty is ±0.1°. This leads to an uncertainty of ±0.001 or ±0.002 in the sines of the angles (you will learn how to calculate these values at the Residential School). You can then calculate the uncertainty in your calculated values for grating spacing, d and wavelength, λ. In Activity D 'The biological effects of gamma radiation', the measurements that you obtain for the lengths of wheat seedlings will have, in addition to measurement uncertainties (because you can only measure to a certain precision), a range of values caused by the inherent variability of the seedlings.

Uncertainties in values can be shown on graphs by means of **error bars**. The value of 57 ± 8 counts per minute given above would be plotted as shown in Figure 3.18. The central point is at 57 counts per minute. The upper end of the error bar is plotted at 57 + 8 = 65 counts per minute and the lower end is plotted at 57 − 8 = 49 counts per minute. The line drawn between the two points spans the range of values consistent with the measured quantity.

3.5.8 Background radiation

A Geiger counter will always detect some radiation whether or not it is pointed at a sample of radioactive material. This is because so-called **background radiation** is around us all the time.

- About 500 000 cosmic rays from outer space penetrate the average person every hour.

- About 30 000 atoms of radioactive radon, polonium, bismuth or lead in the air breathed disintegrate each hour in an average person's lungs.

- About 15 million atoms of potassium-40 and 7000 atoms of uranium from the food eaten disintegrate per hour inside an average person.

- Over 200 million γ-rays from the soil and buildings pass through an average person each hour.

3.5.9 Radiation safety

The radioactive sources that you will use in Activity A are very weak. The strongest source produces about the same number of radioactive decays as the radioactive source in a household smoke detector, namely 40 kilobecquerels (this is equivalent to 40 000 **becquerels** or radioactive decays per second).

We have calculated that the maximum **dose equivalent** of radiation that you might receive during Activity A, as a result of being near the radioactive sources, is less than 1 microsievert (μSv). The definition of the unit of dose equivalent, the **sievert** (Sv), is complex, depending on the absorbed dose in the time you are close to the source and the different biological properties of different types of radiation and particles, but the following comparisons may be of interest.

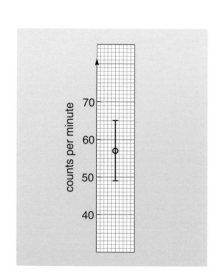

Figure 3.18   A count rate of 57 ± 8 counts per minute plotted on a graph; the uncertainty is shown as an error bar.

- The typical dose equivalent experienced as a result of natural background radiation in the UK is about 6.8 μSv per day, or 21 μSv per day if you live in a location such as Cornwall which has a high concentration of radioactive rocks.

- On a three-hour aeroplane flight you would receive a dose equivalent of about 10 μSv from cosmic rays.

- The dose equivalent that you would receive from a typical chest X-ray is about 20 μSv.

- It is estimated that the instantaneous dose of γ-radiation which some survivors of the Hiroshima and Nagasaki atomic bombs were exposed to was approximately 5 Sv.

- As stated above, we estimate that you will receive a dose equivalent of less than 1 μSv during the experiments in Activity A.

Question 3.3

How many times greater is the dose equivalent received by survivors of the atomic bombs in Japan than the dose equivalent you might receive during Activity A?

In Activity D you will study the effects of γ-radiation on the growth of a species of wheat. The wheat grains for this experiment are exposed to 2 kSv of γ-radiation before they are delivered to the Residential School site.

$$\frac{2 \text{ kSv}}{1 \text{ μSv}} = \frac{2 \times 10^3 \text{ Sv}}{1 \times 10^{-6} \text{ Sv}} = 2 \times 10^9$$

which is 10^9 (a thousand million) times greater than the dose equivalent you might receive in Activity A. However, note that neither the wheat grains nor the plants subsequently grown from them are made radioactive by this treatment and both can be handled with complete safety.

3.5.10 The effect of distance

We can now explain some of the safety precautions detailed in the workbook for Activity A (which you might like to look at now): for example, the instructions to use tongs when handling radioactive samples and to keep samples at the back of your bench when not in use. If you were to use a Geiger counter to count the radiation 1 cm from a point source and then repeat the readings at a distance of 10 cm from the same source, you would find that the count rate would be reduced by a factor of approximately 100. The variation of count rate with distance obeys an **inverse square law**: in other words, the count rate decreases by a factor of x^2 every time the distance increases by a factor of x. So, if you use tongs to handle the uranium-rich mineral encased in resin (see Figure 10 in the workbook for Activity A), your hand will be approximately 20 cm from the mineral rather than at a distance of about 1 cm, so the dose of radiation which you receive will be reduced by a factor of $(20)^2$, i.e. 400.

The marked variation of count rate with distance also explains why it is so important to keep the positions of the Geiger tube and the isotope generator *fixed* when you are investigating the absorption of γ-rays by different thicknesses of lead.

61

3.5.11 The absorption of radioactivity

In Activity A, you will determine the half-life for a radioactive source, but you will also investigate what happens when α- or β-particles or γ-rays pass through different materials. The effectiveness of a material in absorbing γ-rays can be quantified by stating its **half-thickness**. If you plot a graph of count rate against the thickness of lead, say, between a fixed source and a fixed Geiger counter, the resulting graph has the same characteristic shape as when calculating the half-life; and the half-thickness is defined as the thickness of lead needed for the count to halve.

For γ-rays, the half-thickness depends only on the material used and the energy of the source. As the γ-rays pass through the lead they are scattered by the electrons in the metal, transferring some of their energy to the electrons with each encounter. The more electrons there are, the more likely it is that the energy will be transferred, so dense materials with a high atomic number (such as lead with an atomic number of 82) are relatively good absorbers of γ-rays. The net result, therefore, is that the energy of the γ-ray photons is transferred to the lead.

The absorption characteristics of α-particles and electrons differ from those of γ-rays. Alpha-particles are the most readily absorbed, being completely stopped by a single sheet of paper, whereas electrons are absorbed easily by low atomic number materials, such as the carbon atoms in perspex. Neither of these materials is very effective at stopping γ-rays. Lead is an effective absorber of all types of radiation, which is why it is used to shield people from radiation sources in 'lead aprons', etc., and in the boxes used to store the radioactive sources that you will use at the Residential School.

Gamma-rays, α-particles and electrons released in the Earth from radioactive minerals are absorbed by the minerals themselves and the surrounding rocks. Figure 3.19 illustrates the radiation damage that can result. The energy released by radioactive decays in the Earth can be transferred to the Earth itself. You will investigate the amount of energy that is transferred in this way in the final part of Activity A.

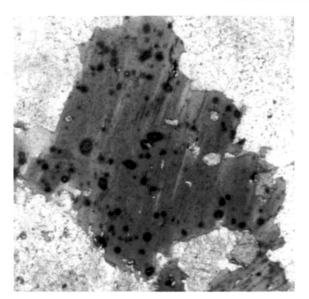

Figure 3.19   Highly magnified thin section of rock showing a brown crystal of biotite mica about 1 mm across. It shows dark spots (called 'pleochroic haloes'), which result from radiation damage caused by the radioactive decay of minute zircon crystals. In some cases, the zircon crystal is visible at the centre of the pleochroic halo.

3.6   Self-assessment questions

Question 3.4

The mass of a proton (m_p) is 1.673×10^{-27} kg and the mass of an electron (m_e) is 9.11×10^{-31} kg. Write the mass of the electron as a fraction of the mass of the proton.

Express your answer in the form $m_e = (1 \div n)m_p$, where n is a whole number quoted to an accuracy of 3 significant figures.

Question 3.5

(a) A vapour of substance X is heated and emits visible light that comprises a spectrum of several coloured lines (each line corresponding to a specific wavelength). Explain the link between this spectrum and the processes taking place in the atoms of substance X.

(b) In the hydrogen spectrum shown in Figure 3.6b, the red spectral line for hydrogen is caused by electrons falling from energy level 3 to energy level 2. If the energy difference $(E_3 - E_2) = 3.03 \times 10^{-19}$ J, what is the wavelength of the red line?

(Assume values of 6.63×10^{-34} J s for the Planck constant, h, and 3.00×10^8 m s^{-1} for the speed of light in a vacuum, c.)

Question 3.6

Light from a laser, with a wavelength of 633 nm, is shone (at 90°) on a diffraction grating with an unknown grating spacing. The angle between the straight through direction and the first order diffraction image is 30.4°. Use this information to calculate the value of the grating's spacing.

Question 3.7

A student measures the speed of a falling stone at time intervals of 0.5 seconds. The data collected is recorded in Table 3.4. (The uncertainty in the time is negligible compared with the uncertainty in the speed measurement.)

Using this data, draw a graph of speed against time on the graph paper in Figure 3.20, and remember to include the error bars to show uncertainties. The gradient of the graph gives the average acceleration of the stone. Use your graph to find this acceleration.

Table 3.4 Data for Question 3.7

Time/s	Speed of stone/m s^{-1}
0	–
0.5	5 ± 1
1.0	10 ± 1
1.5	15 ± 1
2.0	20 ± 1
2.5	26 ± 2
3.0	29 ± 2

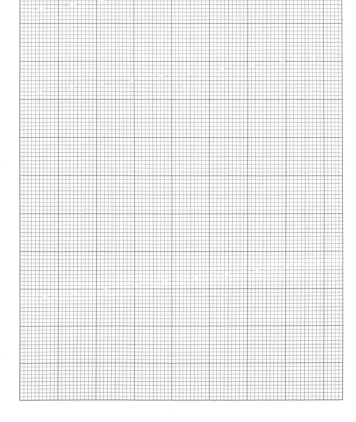

Figure 3.20   Graph paper for use with Question 3.7.

Question 3.8

A student uses a Geiger counter to measure the count rate from an unknown radioactive source. The results are shown in Table 3.5. Complete the table by including the uncertainty in the count rate for each measurement.

Note: for the purposes of this question you should assume that background radiation can be ignored. This will *not* be the case when you are at the Residential School.

Table 3.5 Data for Question 3.8.

Elapsed time/min	Counts per minute	Uncertainty in the count rate per minute
1	403	
2	320	
3	249	
4	201	
5	157	
6	128	
7	109	
8	89	
9	71	
10	66	

Question 3.9

Figure 3.21 shows how a sample of radioactive carbon, $^{14}_{6}C$, decays from its natural state. Use this graph to find the half-life of $^{14}_{6}C$.

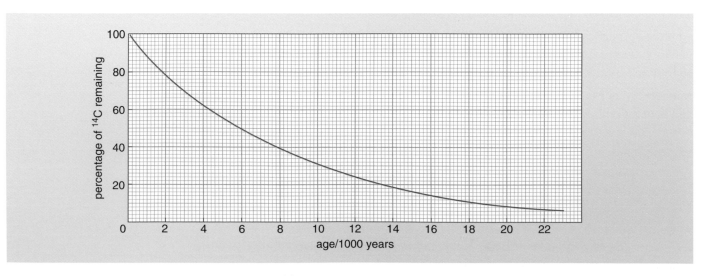

Figure 3.21   The radioactive decay curve of $^{14}_{6}C$.

3.7   What to do next

You can check that you have understood the material in this chapter by working through the online interactive self-assessment questions for Chapter 3. You can access these questions via the link on the SXR103 course website.

You should now read the second half of the workbook for Activity A (from Task 8 onwards).

3.8   Summary of Chapter 3

An atom is a very small structure that is about 10^{-10} m across. It consists of a nucleus, containing protons and neutrons, surrounded by a distribution of negatively charged electrons.

Energy is conserved: thus when an atom changes from a state of higher energy to one of lower energy, a photon with energy corresponding to the atom's loss of energy is emitted.

Different elements have different spectral signatures, consisting of spectral lines of characteristic energies and wavelengths.

A spectrometer is used with a diffraction grating to produce a diffraction pattern. The angle of diffraction, θ_n, for the nth order relates to the grating spacing, d, and the wavelength, λ, by the equation:

$$\sin \theta_n = \frac{n\lambda}{d}$$

Some chemical elements exist in several forms, called isotopes, each with the same atomic number (i.e. the same number of protons) but with a different number of neutrons and hence a different mass number.

Radioactive decay is the process whereby certain unstable nuclei break up or decay spontaneously. The types of decay include α-decay, β^--decay and γ-decay. In any nuclear decay, the electric charge and mass number are always conserved.

An infinitesimal amount of mass, m, is lost in radioactive decays, and this is converted into energy, E, according to the equation $E = mc^2$, where c is the speed of light in a vacuum.

Radioactive decay is an intrinsically random process and it is impossible to know when an individual nucleus will decay. However, with a large enough number of nuclei, the concept of half-life (the time taken for half a radioactive sample to decay) cab be used as a measure of how rapidly the isotope is likely to decay.

A Geiger counter will always detect some radiation whether it is pointed at a source of radioactive material or not. This is because of background radiation, which is around you all the time.

Alpha-particles, beta-particles and gamma-rays are absorbed as they pass through materials. The effectiveness of a particular type of particle or radiation can be measured by quoting its half-thickness.

There is a degree of uncertainty in all experimental measurements. Uncertainties are indicated on graphs by error bars.

The radioactive sources you will use at the Residential School are very weak. Additional safety precautions are based on keeping them at a distance from your body (e.g. by using tongs) and storing them in lead-lined boxes when they are not in use, as lead is a very effective absorber of all types of radiation.

Now that you have completed Chapter 3 you should be able to:

- explain the link between the lines observed in emission spectra and the processes taking place within atoms
- calculate the grating spacing, d, of a diffraction grating from your knowledge of the diffraction order, n, angle of diffraction, θ_n, and wavelength, λ; or calculate an unknown wavelength from your knowledge of d, n and θ_n
- plot a best-fit graph and calculate and interpret the gradient of a straight-line graph
- calculate the uncertainty in a measured value of count rate
- calculate the half-life or half-thickness from an appropriate graph of count rate against time or thickness of absorber
- explain why it is important to keep radioactive sources at a distance from your body, and to store them in a lead-lined container.

Chapter 4
Biology: the science of life

Biology features prominently in two of the five activities in the residential component of *Practising science*: Activity C 'Investigating the environment' and Activity D 'The biological effects of gamma radiation'. Activity C integrates Earth sciences and ecology (the branch of biology concerned with the interaction of living organisms with their environment, including other living organisms) in the context of fieldwork. In contrast, Activity D is a laboratory-based investigation and predominantly biological in nature. Although they are concerned with rather different areas of biological knowledge and use different practical techniques, Activities C and D have several important features in common. For instance, they both require you to make careful observations (both qualitative and quantitative) of living organisms, to record data systematically, and then to propose and test hypotheses that might explain your initial observations.

To ensure that you have the necessary biological knowledge and skills to get the most out of these activities, you should first work through Section 4.1 (which supports Activity D) and then Section 4.2 (which supports Activity C).

4.1   Activity D 'The biological effects of gamma radiation'

Exposure to significant doses of ionising radiation is harmful to life. This is evident from the devastating effects of the nuclear weapons used in Japan at the end of the Second World War, when survivors of the blast continued to die from radiation sickness and leukaemia, and from the increased incidence of thyroid cancer in people after the accident at the nuclear power station at Chernobyl in the Ukraine in 1986. Although such incidents, thankfully, are rare, the development of medical uses of radiation sources for treating cancer and imaging, the use of nuclear fuel for electricity production (and the problem of disposing of radioactive waste) and, of course, the presence of natural background radiation (Sections 3.5.8 and 3.5.9) mean that low levels of radiation are everywhere. To understand the biological consequences of this exposure, it is important to know what radiation does to living tissue and why it causes harm.

The biological effects of exposure to radiation vary with the dose. The typical dose received as a result of average background radiation is approximately 3 mSv per year (see Section 3.5.9 for an explanation of the units). This does not seem to cause any detectable harm whereas an exposure of 1 Sv per hour would result in radiation poisoning. In humans this could include symptoms such as nausea, disorientation, seizures, coma, haemorrhaging, ulceration, infections (due to reduced immunity as a result of damage to white blood cells), sloughing of skin, hair loss and sterility. A dose of between 3 and 5 Sv received over a few minutes will result in death within a few days. A person exposed to 0.1 Sv has a 1 in 200 chance of developing cancer in later life.

The type of radiation and whether the source is inside or outside the body is also important. Alpha- (α) radiation is easily absorbed by cells, and so is quite toxic, but it does not penetrate skin. Beta- (β) and gamma- (γ) radiation will penetrate skin but are less easily absorbed by cells. If the radioactive source is outside the body then β- and particularly γ-radiation are more dangerous than α-radiation since they will penetrate the skin and cause damage to the cells inside the body. Since α-radiation cannot penetrate the skin, it will not reach the living cells beneath. If the radioactive source is swallowed or breathed in then α-radiation is the most dangerous because it is easily absorbed by cells whereas β- and γ-radiation are not.

This gross damage to tissues and organs after high dosages of radiation is a result of changes at the molecular and the cellular level. Radiation can kill whole cells but the most critical damage caused by radiation is to **DNA**. DNA is contained within the nucleus of the cell and it carries the code for all the information needed for the synthesis of proteins, cell reproduction, and for the organisation of tissues and organs. Any damage to DNA molecules can have far-reaching consequences. Radiation can cause breakages in DNA strands. When a DNA molecule is broken, the code to produce specific proteins may be lost. Sometimes the damage can affect an entire **chromosome**, causing it to break and recombine in an abnormal way; sometimes parts of two different chromosomes may be combined. Chromosome abnormalities can cause problems during **mitosis** and **meiosis**, and cell division is impaired. Damage to DNA can lead to genetic changes and to cancer.

In Activity D you will investigate the effects of exposing wheat seedlings to γ-radiation. To prepare for this investigation you must ensure that you are familiar with (i) the basic structure of plant cells (Section 4.1.1) and (ii) the process of cell division, including the details of mitosis (Section 4.1.2). Residential School tutors will assume that you understand the terms given in **bold** here (to indicate that they are defined in the online *Glossary*). Then you should do Part I of Activity D (which is in the workbook) (see Section 4.1.3). Part II is the work you will do in the laboratory, which builds directly on Part I.

4.1.1 Structure of plant cells

Since plants are **multicellular eukaryotes** (as opposed to prokaryotes, such as bacteria), their cells consist of **cytoplasm** (surrounded by a **cell membrane**) and a cell **nucleus** (surrounded by a **nuclear membrane**). Two additional features of plant, but not animal, cells are external **cell walls** made of cellulose (which give the cells their shape and rigidity) and, within the cytoplasm, **chloroplasts** (which are used for **photosynthesis**) (Figure 4.1).

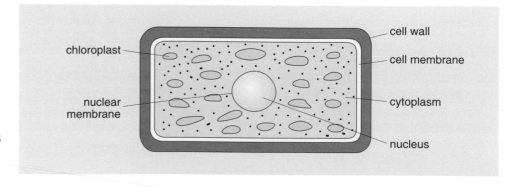

Figure 4.1   Schematic diagram of a typical plant cell. Actively photosynthesising cells contain *many* more chloroplasts than shown here.

4.1.2 Cell division

A plant's genetic information is encoded in DNA, most of which is located in the nucleus. Nuclear DNA is packaged into chromosomes, which – most of the time – comprise two **chromatids** joined at a point called the **centromere** (Figure 4.2). Each chromatid consists of a single, relatively long (but extremely thin) DNA molecule with associated protein molecules. Between cell divisions – in what is called the **interphase** – individual chromosomes cannot be distinguished within the nucleus, even under a microscope.

A plant produced by sexual reproduction starts as a **zygote** formed by the fusion of two **gametes** at fertilisation. Gametes have half the number of chromosomes of the zygote (i.e. they are **haploid**). The zygote and all the cells descended from it are described as **diploid**. Gametes are produced by meiosis, a process that – among other things – halves the number of chromosomes in the resulting **progeny cells**. Figure 4.3 shows how the number of chromosomes changes during meiosis and fertilisation.

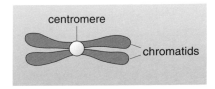

Figure 4.2 Sketch of a single chromosome, showing the two chromatids joined at the centromere.

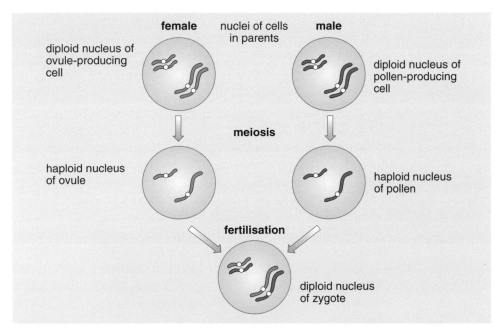

Figure 4.3 Diagram showing how the number of chromosomes changes during meiosis and fertilisation for a hypothetical plant with only two pairs of chromosomes (most species have many more). For simplicity, each chromosome is shown as a single strand, rather than as a pair of chromatids.

All of a plant's cells other than its gametes are produced by mitosis, a process that results in two cells that are identical with the parent cell – and hence one another – in all respects (except for relatively infrequent **mutations**).

The zygote grows in size, undergoes mitosis and then divides into two progeny cells. This sequence (known as the **cell cycle**) is repeated many times (Figure 4.4) to produce first an embryo, then a seedling and ultimately a complete flowering plant.

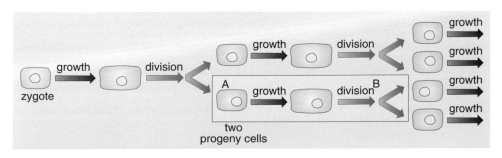

Figure 4.4 Repetition of the cell cycle (i.e. alternation of cell growth and mitotic cell division) enables a zygote to grow into a complete flowering plant.

Mitosis is a continuous process that takes several hours to several tens of hours (depending on the species and the prevailing conditions) but, conventionally, it is divided into four main phases (Figure 4.5).

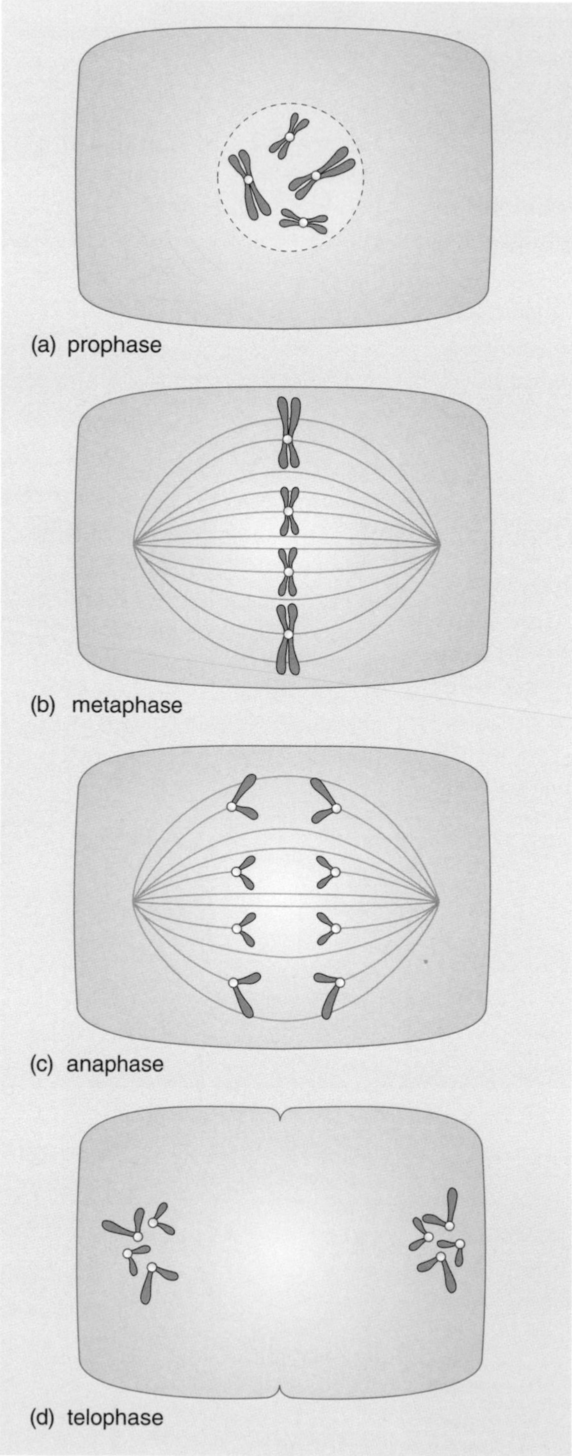

(a) prophase

(b) metaphase

(c) anaphase

(d) telophase

Figure 4.5 The four main phases of mitosis: (a) prophase; (b) metaphase; (c) anaphase; (d) telophase (with cell division itself just starting).

During **prophase** the nuclear membrane disappears and, by coiling of their DNA molecules, the chromosomes become so short and fat (compared with their condition during interphase) that they are readily visible under a microscope (provided suitable stains are used to make them visible) (Figure 4.5a). Each chromosome's centromere then connects to delicate threads attached at each end of the cell. These threads exert a tension that results in the chromosomes becoming aligned across the middle (or 'equator') of the cell (**metaphase**) (Figure 4.5b). The chromatids then separate (the centromere splits), so that each becomes a chromosome in its own right. One member of each former pair of chromatids is drawn to one end of the cell, while its partner is drawn to the other end (**anaphase**) (Figure 4.5c). Once the chromatids reach one or other end of the cell, the threads that were attached to them disappear. There is now a set of single-chromatid chromosomes at one end of the cell and an equivalent set at the other end (**telophase**; Figure 4.5d).

The DNA molecules then uncoil again, causing the chromosomes to disappear from view. At the same time, a nuclear membrane forms around each cluster of chromosomes so that the cell temporarily contains two nuclei. Mitosis is now complete but the cell itself must still divide in two (i.e. each nucleus and its surrounding cytoplasm must become completely surrounded by a cell membrane and a cell wall). The two progeny cells – each of which contains an identical copy of the parent cell's genetic material – are now in interphase (see Figure 4.1). Before the progeny cells can undergo mitosis, their DNA molecules must be replicated (i.e. their single-chromatid chromosomes must become two-chromatid chromosomes; see Figure 4.2).

4.1.3 Activity D Part I

You should now work through Part I of Activity D (i.e. Stages 1–4 in the workbook). When you have finished, you should study the preparatory material for the ecology part of Activity C 'Investigating the environment' (in Section 4.2 of this book).

4.2   What is ecology?

The word **ecology** is derived from two Greek words: *oikos*, meaning home, and *logos*, meaning understanding. This suggests that ecology is the study of the surroundings, or the environment, in which organisms live. However, organisms are not passive in relation to their environment but will interact with it, responding to environmental changes and even causing environmental change themselves. So a better definition of ecology is that it is the study of interactions between organisms and their environment. These interactions can be divided into two main types: interactions with the physical and the chemical environment (**abiotic** interactions) and interactions with other living organisms (**biotic** interactions).

4.2.1 Biotic interactions

A familiar biotic interaction is **predation**. A predator can influence the abundance of a prey species and, in some circumstances, may be important in regulating the size of the prey population. Figure 4.6 shows the results of a study in southern England into the effects on rabbit abundance of gamekeepers removing predators (mainly foxes, stoats and cats).

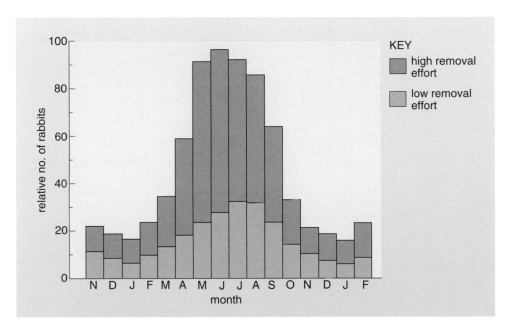

Figure 4.6   Average rabbit numbers throughout a year at sites in southern England where the effort put into predator removal was either high or low.

■ What can be deduced about the effect of predators on rabbit numbers from Figure 4.6?

☐ The removal of predators led to a noticeable increase in rabbit numbers, especially between the months of May and August.

An interesting point to note here is that the predators were being removed in order to protect game species, such as pheasant, but this action had an unintentional knock-on effect on the rabbit population. This highlights how important it is to understand how species interact when attempting to manage wild populations for farming or conservation reasons.

Animals feeding on plants, or **herbivory**, not only affects the abundance of vegetation but also can affect the composition of species present. Figure 4.7 shows sketches of two grassland plots; one was fenced to exclude rabbits for six years; the other was unfenced and so was grazed by rabbits. They were drawn by the pioneering English ecologist Sir Arthur Tansley (1871–1955).

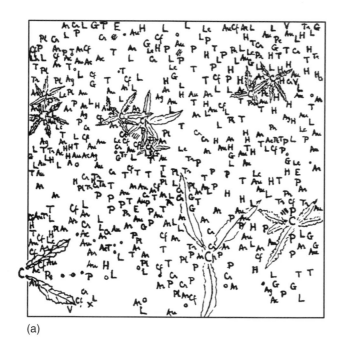

(a)

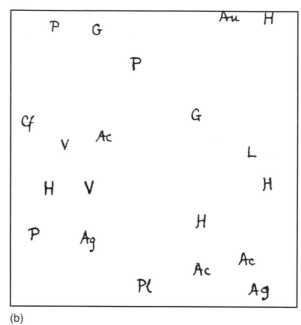

(b)

Figure 4.7   (a) A 25 cm × 25 cm plot of grassland under moderately heavy grazing pressure from rabbits. (b) A similar plot after rabbits and other grazing animals were excluded for six years. Each letter represents the shoot of a broadleaved plant. Different species have different letters and letter size reflects plant size. The leaf rosettes marked 'C' indicate stemless thistle (*Cirsium acaule*) and the one marked 'Cp' is marsh thistle (*Cirsium palustre*). The spaces between the shoots shown are filled with sheep's fescue grass (*Festuca ovina*).

■   Look carefully at the two sketches in Figure 4.7 and summarise the differences between the two plots.

☐   The grazed plot has:

many more shoots of broadleaved plants (441 compared with only 20 in the ungrazed plot)

many more species (21 compared to only 10 in the ungrazed plot)

thistles, which do not occur in the ungrazed plot

a smaller area of *Festuca ovina*

smaller individuals of the species found in both plots (e.g. P, H and L).

This example shows that removing a single species can have far-reaching effects on the other species present.

Competition arises when individual organisms require a shared resource which is in limited supply. Competition between species can influence their distribution. In another classic experiment, Tansley studied two species of bedstraw: heath bedstraw (*Galium saxatile* ('*hercynicum*')), which grows on acidic soils, and slender bedstraw (*G. pumilum*), which grows on calcareous soils. Under experimental conditions, both species could thrive on either soil, provided they were grown separately. However, if both were grown together then only heath bedstraw would grow successfully on acid soil and only slender bedstraw would grow successfully on calcareous soil. This is an example of **competitive exclusion**, where one species prevents another from maintaining a viable population.

Organisms also interact by cooperating to the mutual benefit of both partners in the relationship. Such an interaction is a **mutualism**. **Lichens** are a good example of such an interaction. Although lichens look like, and function as if they are, a single organism they are in fact two organisms (Figure 4.8). The main body of a lichen is a fungus but within the fungal body there is a layer of cells of either photosynthetic algae or **cyanobacteria** (Figure 4.9). Both partners benefit from this relationship. Fungi cannot photosynthesise but they can absorb the products of photosynthesis produced by the alga. The alga is protected by the body of the fungus from excessive solar radiation and from drying out. As a result, the lichen can thrive in extreme and harsh environments where neither the alga nor the fungus could survive on their own.

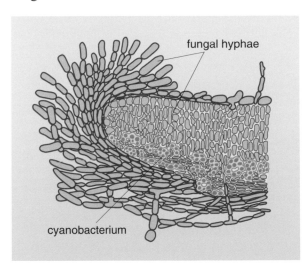

Figure 4.9 Diagram of a lichen containing a cyanobacterial partner.

4.2.2 Abiotic interactions

The ecological fieldwork you will do for Activity C at the Residential School will involve studying *either* two types of grassland (if you are at Sussex University) *or* a rocky seashore (if you are at Heriot-Watt University). Next you will look at some abiotic factors, which are important in these habitats.

Soil properties

Plants derive nutrients (as mineral elements) and water from the soil, so the physical and chemical properties of the soil that plants are growing in are very important in determining which species of plant are likely to be found at a particular site.

Soil is derived partly from accumulated decaying vegetation (the organic component) and partly from broken-up fragments of the underlying rocks (the mineral component). So the underlying geology can have an important influence on soil properties and hence which plant species are present.

Since rocks differ in their chemical composition, the proportions of the different mineral elements in the soils derived from them also vary. For example,

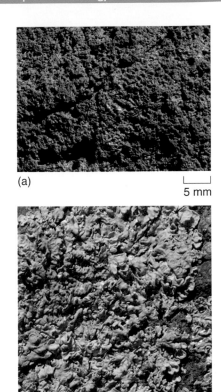

Figure 4.8 Some common lichen species of rocky shores: (a) *Verrucaria* sp. is a crustose lichen. It adheres so closely to the rock surface that it can be difficult to distinguish it from the rock. This lichen is sometimes called the black tar lichen since it looks like a black stain on the rock. (b) *Xanthoria* sp. is a foliose (leaf-like) lichen. (c) *Ramalina* sp. is a fruticose (shrub-like) lichen.

weathering of the mineral **apatite** will supply phosphorus to the soil. Rocks such as granite, which are rich in aluminosilicates, contain a lot of aluminium which can lead to aluminium toxicity problems in certain soils.

Soil texture (the relative proportions of various sized particles in the soil) is mainly determined by the size of the rock particles in the soil. Soil particles can be classified into three main sizes (diameters): sand particles are 2.0–0.02 mm; silt particles are 0.02–0.002 mm; and clay particles are ≤0.002 mm. The bigger the average size of the particles, the coarser the texture and the more free-draining the soil tends to be. Soils with smaller particles are finer textured and more water retentive.

■ Which would be better for plant growth in a dry climate: a sandy or a clayey soil?

☐ The clayey soil would be better because it is more likely to retain moisture during dry periods.

The **pH** (a measure of acidity or alkalinity; see Section 5.2) is another important soil property. Soil pH is determined by both the organic soil components and the water filling the spaces between solid soil particles but it is also influenced by the underlying geology.

■ How would you expect the pH of soil overlying limestone (or chalk, which is a particular form of limestone) to compare with the pH of soil overlying **sandstone**?

☐ The soils will have different pH values. Limestone is a calcareous rock rich in **carbonates** (usually calcite), which gives rise to soils of pH of 7 and above. Sandstones contain much **silica** and so give rise to neutral or slightly acid soils, where the pH can be as low as 3.5.

The pH is a critical factor for plants, since it affects the solubility of mineral nutrients and hence their availability to plants. Figure 4.10 shows, in the form of 'kite' diagrams, the relative availability of several minerals at different pH values. A mineral is most available at pH values where its 'kite' is widest and least available where its 'kite' is narrowest or non-existent.

■ Which elements are likely to be least available to plants growing in low pH (pH 5) soil?

☐ Potassium, sulfur, calcium, magnesium and phosphorus are least available at low pH (pH 5).

■ Which elements are likely to be least available to plants growing in high pH (pH 8.5) soil?

☐ Copper, zinc, iron, manganese, boron and phosphorus are least available at high pH (pH 8.5).

Where minerals are absent at low pH it is often the result of their high solubility in water at these pH values. Consequently, they are carried down through the soil dissolved in water (a process called **leaching**) and enter the groundwater some way below the level of plant roots. In contrast, phosphorus, manganese and boron

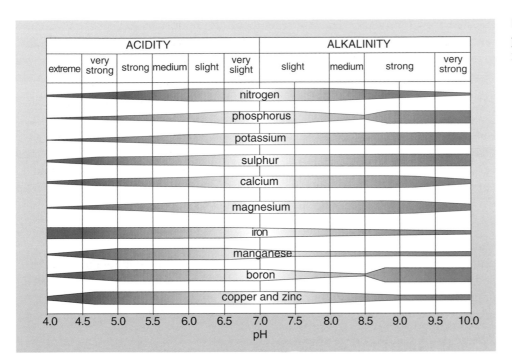

Figure 4.10 Availability to plants of some mineral nutrients in soils of different pH.

are locked up in insoluble iron and aluminium phosphates at around pH 7.5. Plants growing in these soils can have deficiency diseases (e.g. phosphorus deficiency, which shows as yellowing of the leaves). This is particularly true of plants that are not adapted to grow at high pH. Phosphorus is also unavailable at low pH; again it is locked up as insoluble aluminium phosphate.

Animals are also affected by soil pH. Figure 4.11 shows the distribution of earthworm species in soils of different pH. You can see that some species have wide pH tolerances, whereas others have much narrower ranges, being specialist species of either acidic or more neutral soils.

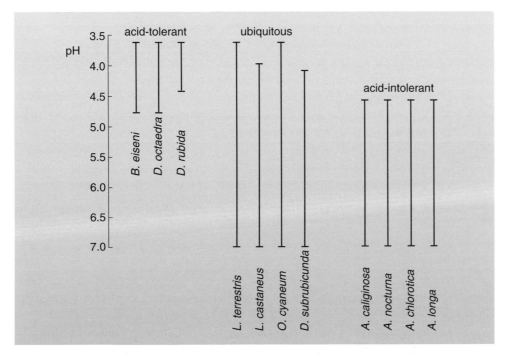

Figure 4.11 Distribution of earthworm species in soils of different pH. (Key: *B. = Bimastos*; *D. = Dendrobaena*; *L. = Lumbricus*; *O. = Octolasium*; *A. = Allobophora*.)

(a)

(b)

(c)

Figure 4.12 Three calcicoles (species that are restricted to calcarious soils): (a) wild thyme (*Thymus praecox*) (b) viper's bugloss (*Echium vulgare)* (c) squinancywort (*Asperula cynanchica*).

Species of plants and animals that are found only in alkaline environments are termed **calcicoles** (i.e. organisms that like a calcium-rich environment), whereas those that dislike these soils are called **calcifuges** (i.e. calcium escapers). Typical calcicoles are found in chalk grassland where the soil has a high pH, e.g. viper's bugloss (*Echium vulgare*), squinancywort (*Asperula cynanchica*) and wild thyme (*Thymus praecox*) (Figure 4.12).

Low pH values are a feature of moorlands characterised by common heather or ling (*Calluna vulgaris*), cross-leaved heath (*Erica tetralix*) and bracken (*Pteridium aquilinum*), and of upland bogs characterised by rushes (*Juncus* spp.) and cotton sedge (*Eriophorum vaginatum*), where the pH can be below 5.5 (Figure 4.13).

The reasons why plants show preferences for acid or alkaline soils are not always simple, i.e. not attributable solely to nutrient availability. For instance, some minerals can be toxic. Thus calcicoles grown on acid soils experience aluminium and other toxicities that stunt their root systems. This stunting reduces nutrient uptake as a secondary effect.

When considering the effects of abiotic factors, it is easy to forget that there may also be biotic factors. For example, calcicole and calcifuge species may be able to grow on both types of soil but grow better on one type and are excluded from the other because of competition (see the example of bedstraw in Section 4.2.1). Also, plant species respond in different ways to the availability of nutrients in the soil. Nutrient-responsive species, such as stinging nettle (*Urtica dioica*), grow slowly on nutrient-poor soils but very fast indeed on nutrient-rich soils. As a result, they are strong competitors on nutrient rich soils and tend to be the dominant species in this situation. On the other hand, they do not thrive on nutrient-poor soils, such as is the case in chalk grassland, so other, slower-growing species can survive.

Salinity, desiccation and biotic interactions on seashores

Tidal movements ensure that seashore habitats are, even if not covered by seawater for part of each day, at least subject to spray-borne salt and wind. So, even well above the level of high tides, seashore organisms need to be more tolerant of salt than most terrestrial organisms. However, salinity (the concentration of salts dissolved in water) is not the only factor affecting seashore species. Seaweeds and shelled animals such as limpets and barnacles are adapted to living in a highly saline marine environment, but they become desiccated (dry out) if they are out of water for too long between high tides. There is a gradual decrease in salinity and an increase in the danger of desiccation from the sea to the land. Figure 4.14 shows how the distribution of some seashore animals is affected by this gradual environmental change.

■ Which species is present below the lowest tide level?

☐ Only the blue-rayed limpet (*Patella aspersa*) is present below the lowest tide level.

■ Which species is most **abundant** between the average low-tide level and the mean-tide level?

☐ The common limpet (*Patella vulgata*) is the most abundant species between the average low-tide level and the mean-tide level.

- Which species are present above the highest tide level (the **supralittoral zone**)?

☐ Only periwinkles, barnacles and common limpets are present above the highest tide level. Periwinkles are the most abundant species on this part of the shore. The other species are present only in very low numbers.

Figure 4.14 shows how the gradual change in salinity and the danger of desiccation affect the distribution of animal species on the shore. Note how none of the species is equally abundant for the full length of the shore. Some are more abundant on the lower part of the shore, where they are only uncovered by water for a short time each day. Others are more abundant on the upper part of the shore, where they are uncovered for longer. This results in a characteristic distribution where different species of animals and plants

Figure 4.13 Cross-leaved heath (*Erica tetralix*), a calcifuge, which is restricted to habitats with acidic, often peaty soils.

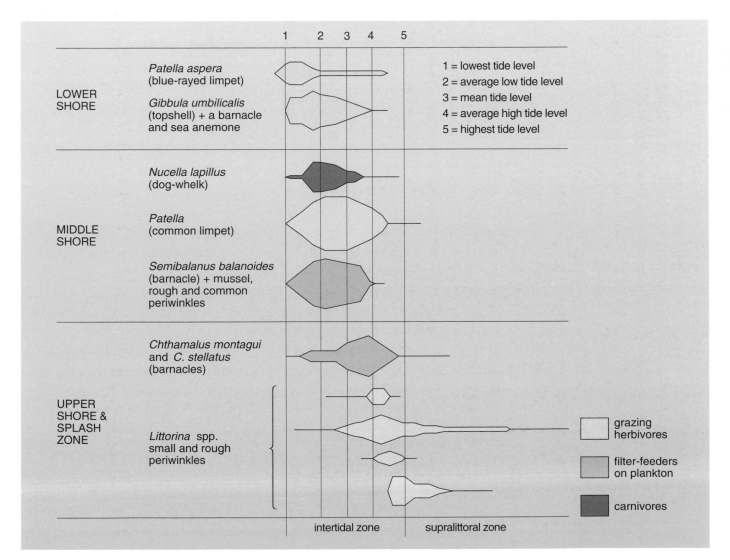

Figure 4.14 Kite diagram showing the mean distribution of animals on rocky shores of the Dale peninsula, Pembrokeshire, Wales. The width (on the *y*-axis) of each lozenge-shaped 'kite' indicates the relative abundance of that animal.

terrestrial vegetation
grey lichen
yellow lichen
black lichen
spiral wrack

egg wrack

serrated wrack and kelp

Figure 4.15   Zonation of seaweeds and lichens on a rocky shore at Aberdour, Fife, Scotland. Note the bands of light and dark coloured seaweeds and the band of yellow lichens at the top of the shore.

are arranged in bands at right angles (perpendicular) to the direction of environmental change. This distribution is called **zonation** (Figure 4.15).

Zonation is not simply a result of different species having different tolerances to certain environmental conditions. The lower part of the shore is covered by the sea more often and so more organisms live here. This means there is intense competition for the limited space available.

Pelvetia canaliculata (channelled wrack) is a seaweed that normally occurs high on the shore around the position of the average high-tide level. In experiments on the Isle of Cumbrae in Scotland, *P. canaliculata* was transplanted further down the shore in the area where *Fucus spiralis* (spiral wrack) is normally abundant. If *F. spiralis* had been cleared from the site then the *P. canaliculata* zygotes settled and germinated readily. However, as *F. spiralis* grew back, *P. canaliculata* gradually died out. If *F. spiralis* was prevented from returning then the *P. canaliculata* survived and grew well. This suggests that one reason *P. canaliculata* does not occur lower down the shore is because it cannot compete against faster-growing species.

Limpet distribution is linked to the heavy growth of brown seaweeds, such as wracks and kelps. When juvenile limpets (spat) are released into seawater they must settle on rock surfaces to develop further. If all rock surfaces are covered in seaweed, there is nowhere for them to settle.

As well as having to face intense competition, organisms living on the lower shore are also subjected to more herbivory and predation. Organisms that can protect themselves from desiccation can live higher up the shore and are subjected to less competition and predation. So zonation is the result of an interaction between both abiotic and biotic factors. The upper boundaries of each zone are usually determined by the degree of tolerance to abiotic factors and the lower boundaries are usually determined by biotic factors.

Although zonation occurs on all rocky shores the pattern of zonation can vary. A common reason for this is exposure to wave action. If the shore is in an exposed location (i.e. a high energy environment), seashore organisms need to be able to tolerate severe abrasion caused by both wave action and pebble movements.

Figure 4.16 shows the zonation pattern of seaweeds and grazing animals on two rocky shores, one of which is sheltered and the other is exposed.

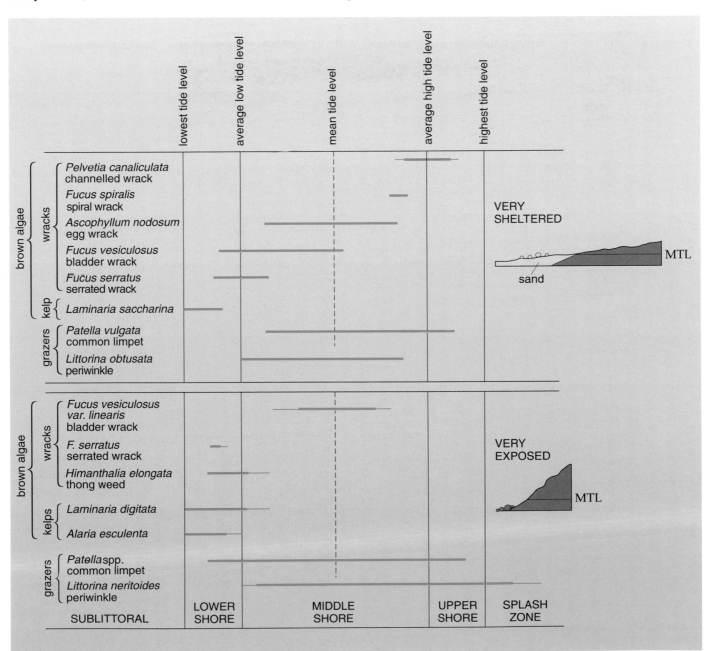

Figure 4.16   Generalised zonation pattern of seaweeds (algae) and grazing animals on two rocky shores (MTL = mean tide level).

■ What are the main differences in the pattern of zonation on the two shores?

☐ Both grazers have a greater vertical distribution than any of the seaweeds, especially on the exposed shore. *Pelvetia canaliculata* is absent from the exposed shore. This is a slow-growing species so it is less able to recover from damage by wave action. There are many more species of seaweed present on the middle shore of the sheltered shore than on the exposed shore.

It is tempting to conclude that wave action alone is responsible for the differences in the distribution of seaweeds on the two shores. However, it is not as simple as that. Look at Figure 4.17. It shows the zonation pattern on three shores with three different levels of exposure.

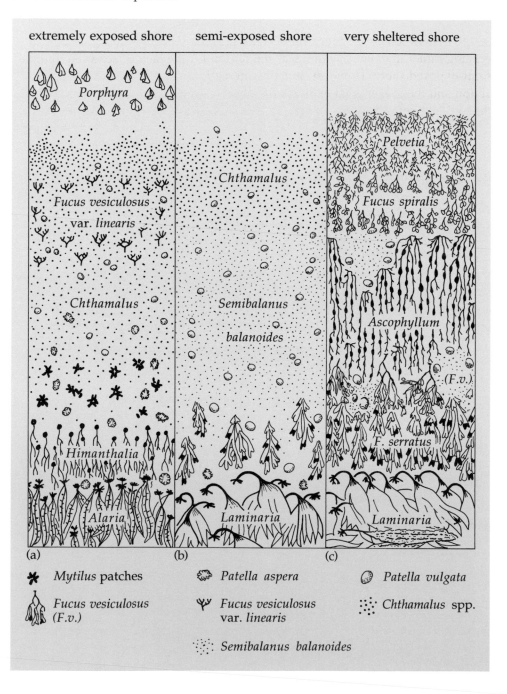

Figure 4.17   Main zonation of seaweeds and animals on three types of seashore in the Dale area of Pembrokeshire.

■ What is odd about the semi-exposed shore?

☐ There are no seaweeds on the middle and upper shore of the semi-exposed shore. Some seaweeds are present at these positions on the exposed shore, so you would expect a steady increase in the abundance of seaweeds from the exposed to the sheltered shore but this is not the case.

This could suggest that there is another factor at work here in addition to exposure to wave action. An experiment on a semi-exposed shore on Holy Island near Anglesey suggests that a biotic factor could also be operating. This shore had a low cover of seaweed but a high density of limpets. All of the limpets were removed from part of this shore and recolonisation was prevented for a year. Within the year the area where limpets had been removed had 80–90% seaweed cover. Since limpets are grazers, this suggests that limpet grazing rather than wave action was the reason for the lack of seaweed in the semi-exposed shore. However, it is the interaction between the effects of wave action and the grazers that explains the observation. On the exposed shore, only the toughest seaweeds can survive the effects of wave action, but the grazers are also suppressed by wave action. This permits a sparse covering of seaweeds to develop. On the semi-exposed shore, the seaweeds are reduced to some extent by wave action but the grazers are not suppressed so they can prevent fresh colonisation by young seaweeds. On the sheltered shore, conditions are favourable for the rapid growth of seaweeds. The rocks are densely covered in seaweed so there are no bare patches available for limpets to become established.

To summarise, ecology is the study of quite complex interactions between organisms and their environment. Often these interactions have unexpected outcomes. It is important to understand these interactions. Without an understanding the reasons why different habitats continue to function, why organisms occur where they do, and why they increase or decline in numbers, it is impossible to identify or conserve threatened species. Equally, without this understanding, it is often not possible to make judgements on environmental issues affecting humans.

4.2.3 Carrying out an ecological investigation

As part of SXR103 you will carry out an ecological investigation. This section will show you how an ecologist begins and plans the study of a new site. This will prepare you for when you have to do this yourself.

The best way to describe how an ecologist works is to consider an example of an actual ecological investigation.

Figures 4.18 and 4.19 show different areas of a deciduous woodland in Co. Donegal, Ireland. This woodland has a particularly attractive ground **flora** including plants such as bluebells (*Hyacinthoides non-scripta*), wood anemone (*Anemone nemorosa*), primrose (*Primula vulgaris*), and pignut (*Conopodium majus*). It was suspected that this ground flora was declining, so the aim of the study was to investigate what might be happening in the woodland which may be affecting the abundance of any of the ground flora species.

Figure 4.18   The northwest area of the woodland. Note the attractive ground flora, which includes bluebells and other flowering plants but shrubby salmonberry (see Box 4.1) is absent.

Figure 4.19   The eastern part of the woodland. Note that bluebells are present in isolated patches and the understorey is dominated by salmonberry.

Making and recording initial observations

The first stage in any ecological study is to do a preliminary survey of the site. This means walking over the site systematically, carefully observing the topographic features, and which organisms and habitats are present.

It is important to record these observations so that anyone returning to the site at a later date will know where the observations were made and so whether there have been any changes at the site. They will also understand how these initial observations led to any subsequent investigations.

The field notes should include the following information.

- The precise location and grid reference (so that you can return to the same area if you need to do so).

- The date and time of the observation.

- The weather conditions (this information could explain why some organisms that you expected to find were absent).

- A description of the topography, e.g. is the soil surface more or less even? Does it undulate or are there deep depressions? Is the site on a slope?

- A general description of the soil and, if possible, any information about the underlying geology.

- The aspect of the site, i.e. whether it is facing north or south. This is particularly important when studying deep valleys or cuttings where the south-facing bank is in the sun for the hotter part of the day, so the soil will be drier than on the north-facing side.

- If you are investigating a seashore environment, you would also record the time in relation to the state of the tide (e.g. an hour before low tide, two hours after high tide).

- Whether the site is exposed to or sheltered from wind and waves.

A list of species seen during the walk-over survey should also be compiled.

It is usually good practice to include a simple, annotated sketch of the site. Such a sketch is not intended to be a work of art but is simply a quick way of making detailed notes on-site. It should be a plan drawing of the site (i.e. an aerial view) which shows areas where different habitats are present and annotated to show key features. Symbols can be used to denote features such as areas where particular species are common or areas with different soil or underlying geology. An approximate scale and the position of north should be shown. A topographic profile of the site can be shown with a small inset drawing of an imaginary lateral view.

In the study of the Irish woodland the initial observations showed that there were parts of the wood where there was a thriving and diverse ground flora and other parts where the ground flora were not so abundant or had a patchy distribution (Figure 4.20). The investigators decided from their initial observations that two factors were possibly influencing the abundance of the ground flora. On the east side of the woodland there was an area of boggy ground where a stream overflowed into the woodland. There was very little ground flora in this area. On the west side of the woodland the **understorey** was dominated by salmonberry (*Rubus spectabilis*), as described in Box 4.1.

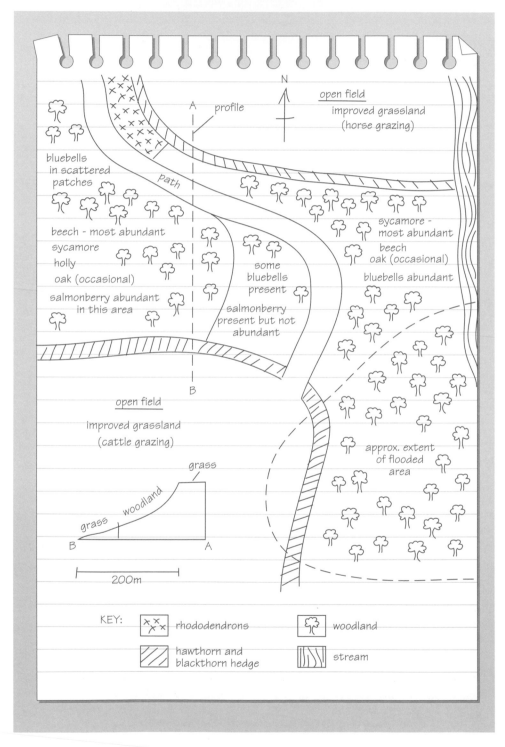

Figure 4.20   Initial field sketch of the woodland.

Box 1 Salmonberry

Salmonberry (*Rubus spectabilis*) is a North American species introduced
to Ireland as an ornamental plant, usually in the grounds of large houses.
It is related to wild raspberry but is instantly recognisable by its distinctive
yellow fruits (Figure 4.21). It is an invasive species, and in parts of
Northern Ireland it has come to dominate the understorey of deciduous
woodland. It is tolerant of medium to heavy shade. It partially dies back in
winter but in spring it grows quickly and establishes a dense leafy sward
to exploit the early springtime light before the woodland canopy closes
over. Because it is an erect, and fairly tall, plant there is a danger that it will
shade out all other plants beneath it, including ground flora species such as
bluebells, which also depend on the availability of light in spring.

Figure 4.21 Salmonberry
(*Rubus spectabilis*): note the distinctive
yellow fruit.

Although salmonberry was present in other parts of the wood, it was not as
abundant in those areas as it was in the western part of the woodland. Up to this
stage in the investigation only qualitative (non-numerical) observations have
been made. Although these are sufficient to make the investigators suspect these
possible explanations, they are based purely on subjective judgements, which
can be misleading. For instance, you might be influenced by the 'attractiveness'
of a species or the prominence of its location; you may be attracted by plants in
flower, which are more easily noticed than those not in flower, or have noticed
large day-flying insects which are more obvious than small species that tend to
hide under stones during the day; or you may be influenced simply through bias,
that is finding what you think you *ought* to find. In order to avoid such bias, it is
important to collect quantitative (numerical) data which will ensure an unbiased
assessment.

The investigators therefore decided to carry out quantitative investigations into
both factors: the boggy area and the salmonberry.

Constructing hypotheses and null hypotheses

Having proposed two possible explanations for the decline of the ground flora
in this woodland, the investigators began the next step in their investigation – to
construct hypotheses.

A **hypothesis** is a prediction of what you would expect to find if your proposed explanation of what is happening is correct. Scientists use hypotheses to help them design their experiments and investigations.

■   If the investigators' suspicion that the establishment of salmonberry in the wood has reduced the abundance of other ground flora species is correct, what would you expect to find?

☐   You would expect other ground flora species to be least abundant in sites where salmonberry is established.

■   If the flooding of part of the woodland has reduced the abundance of ground flora species in general, what would you expect to find?

☐   You would expect all ground flora species to be least abundant in the flooded parts of the woodland.

These predictions must be refined further to help design the investigation and ensure the question can be analysed statistically. To do this the hypothesis must answer the following three questions.

1   Will you test for a difference or a **correlation** (whereby the value of one quantity will increase (or decrease) as the value of another quantity increases (or decreases))?

2   What will you measure?

3   What is being compared or correlated?

Now you should try to refine the hypotheses for the two investigations in the woodland.

Figures 4.18 and 4.19 show that there are areas of the woodland where salmonberry is well established and areas where it is almost absent. The best approach here is to compare a site where salmonberry is established with a site where it is not established to see whether there is a difference in the abundance of any of the other ground flora species. Bluebell is the most abundant ground flora species in the woodland, so the researchers decided to use this species for the comparison.

You can now answer the three questions. You are looking for a difference. You are measuring the abundance of bluebells and comparing a site where salmonberry is established with a site where it is not established.

So the hypothesis is:

> There is a difference in the abundance of bluebells at a site where salmonberry is established compared with a site where it is not established.

For the second investigation the researchers had a problem. Most of this woodland is on a slope. However, the flooded area is flat. It was not possible to find a similarly flat but dry part of the woodland to compare with the flooded area. This time they decided to take a different approach. They noticed that as they walked away from the flooded area, the soil became gradually drier. They decided to use this observation to see whether there was a correlation between the dryness of the soil and the abundance of the ground flora species. Again they decided to look at how bluebells were affected and to measure the percentage soil moisture content.

■ What is the hypothesis for this second investigation?

☐ There is a correlation between the abundance of bluebells and the percentage moisture content of the soil.

The null hypothesis

A hypothesis that is to be tested statistically needs to be expressed as a **null hypothesis**. This is because statistical tests work on the assumption that, whatever the observation, it has simply happened by chance alone. In other words, there is an assumption that *no* statistically significant difference or correlation has been found. It is important to understand this so that you interpret the outcome of the statistical test correctly.

You have already constructed your working hypotheses for the two possible investigations. The null hypothesis for the investigation into the effects of flooding in the woodland is:

> There is no significant correlation between the abundance of bluebells and the percentage moisture content of the soil.

■ What is the null hypothesis for the salmonberry investigation?

☐ There is no significant difference in the abundance of bluebells at a site where salmonberry is established compared with a site where it is not established.

Designing your investigation – sampling

On a small site it may be possible to survey a complete population: for example, in a small wood it is possible to count all the trees present. However, this is very rare. Usually the size of the populations to be measured is unmanageably large, so the length of time and the amount of effort needed for a complete survey is prohibitive. Normally, it is necessary to study only part of the site and to generalise from this to the whole area.

However, there are problems with this. Sampling can introduce bias (e.g. soil on slopes and banks tends to be drier than soil in flatter areas). If only plants on banks were sampled there would be a bias towards plant species that tolerate drier conditions. To avoid bias, it is necessary to ensure that the area sampled is representative of the whole site.

Ecological data is often more variable than data from chemistry or physics experiments, so it is very important to collect enough reliable information to analyse dependably. There are statistical techniques to help decide the minimum sample size but a simple rule is that you should sample at least 2% of the area.

Collecting quantitative data

Vegetation is usually sampled with a **quadrat**. This is simply a frame (often, but not always, in the shape of a square) which is used to mark out a standard area on the ground (Figure 4.22a).

Within a quadrat various measures of abundance can be recorded such as:

- counts of the actual numbers of each species present
- frequency of occurrence – the presence or absence of a species within several quadrats
- cover – the area of ground covered by each species.

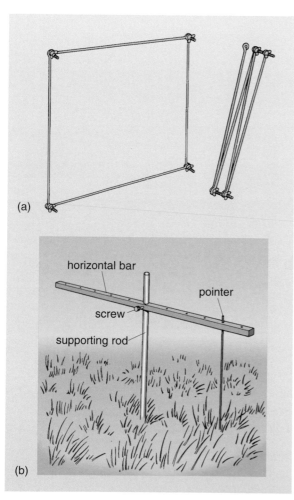

(a)

(b)

Figure 4.22 (a) A convenient, collapsible design of a frame quadrat. (b) A point quadrat.

Sometimes a gridded quadrat is used. This is a quadrat divided into a grid of smaller squares with string or wire. The grid can be used to either estimate cover or measure the local frequency of occurrence. This measure is based on the presence or absence of a species in each of the small squares of the grid.

The size of a quadrat can be important. Often this is determined by the size of the plants you are recording. If you are recording trees, you could measure out a quadrat of 10 m × 10 m; 1 m × 1 m might be suitable for grassland and 10 cm × 10 cm is more suitable for sampling lichens. However, there is another factor to be considered when choosing the size of a quadrat. The larger it is, the more time you need to work through each quadrat. There are advantages to using a small quadrat: it requires less time to work through and it is easier to estimate abundance accurately. However, the disadvantage of using a small quadrat is that it probably won't include some species present at a site in the sample. So a basic principle of sampling is that it is better to use numerous small quadrats rather than a few large quadrats. This is the principle behind the **point quadrat** (Figure 4.22b). This consists of a bar with a series of holes in it. A pin is passed through each hole in turn. Each plant species touched by the pin, as it passes through the vegetation, is recorded as being present at that point. This represents the smallest possible size of quadrat. Point quadrats can be used quickly so a large number of small samples can be taken in a reasonable time span.

The next question is how to plan the sampling. In other words, how do you decide where to place the quadrats on the ground? This is a more important question than it seems because it is very easy to introduce bias into your sampling unintentionally unless it is properly planned in advance. For example, it is tempting to choose the areas with the most interesting or conspicuous vegetation and to ignore areas of bare ground. This could introduce a bias that would overestimate the total amount of vegetation and the abundance of some species at the site and underestimate the abundance of others. Throwing a quadrat over your shoulder means that only vegetation within the distance of your throw is likely to be sampled. (It is also dangerous!) It is important to establish a set of rules for choosing the position of the quadrats beforehand so that a minimum of subjective decisions have to be made on site.

Two sampling plans often used by ecologists are random sampling and systematic sampling.

Random sampling is often used to investigate a possible difference between two, or more, sites (Figure 4.23a). One, or more, (usually square) plots which are representative of the vegetation on each site are marked out on the ground with tape measures or ropes. By measuring (or pacing) along two sides of each plot co-ordinates can be located for quadrat positions within the plot. The co-ordinates used are chosen from random numbers obtained from a table of random numbers or generated by a calculator.

Systematic sampling differs from random sampling in that quadrats are placed on the ground at set intervals. The most common form of systematic sampling is a **transect**. A transect is a straight line measured out across a site. Quadrats are placed at set intervals along the line, say every metre or half metre depending on the length of the transect. Transects are used where there is a gradual change in an environmental variable that you suspect relates to a change in the vegetation (Figure 4.23b): in others words, if you are investigating a possible correlation between an environmental variable and a change in vegetation .

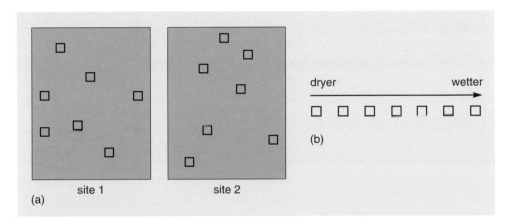

Figure 4.23   Diagram of (a) random and (b) systematic sampling.

Question 4.1

Look back at the null hypotheses for the two possible investigations in the Irish woodland and, in each case, decide whether a transect or random sampling is more appropriate.

Once you have decided on the type of investigation and collected your data, you will analyse it to see whether it supports or disproves your hypothesis.

4.2.4 Data handling and presentation

As with most biological studies, it is usually necessary to analyse ecological data statistically. Why is the use of statistics necessary in ecology? Unfortunately, it is impossible to count all the organisms present at any field site. For example, to find out how many lesser celandines (a yellow-flowered plant related to buttercups often seen in woodland in spring) are present on a given area of woodland, you need to count the number present in small sample areas of the wood and use these samples to estimate the total population size.

Statistics are used to help determine how reliable these estimates are. If you want to compare the numbers of primroses in two different woodlands, statistics can help decide whether any differences observed are simply due to chance or whether there may be biological or environmental reasons for them. All biological data is inherently variable. Data collected in the field is even more variable than laboratory data since measurements taken in the field are not so precise and many factors which cannot be controlled have to be taken into account. Taking just a few measurements does not provide sufficiently accurate information, therefore many measurements are needed. Statistics are used as a tool to summarise these large amounts of data and help find patterns in it.

Median and range

Two simple statistics – the median and the range – will be used to summarise the data in Activity C. The best way to explain this is to use some data (Table 4.1).

Table 4.1 Frequency of lesser celandine (*Ranunculus ficaria*) recorded at two sites in the same woodland.

	Frequency								
Site 1	22	31	14	28	20	22	16	27	19	
Site 2	21	26	30	13	17	27	17	17	29	23

The data in Table 4.1 shows some frequency measurements of lesser celandine at two sites in the same wood. Nine quadrats were used at Site 1 and ten quadrats were used at Site 2. Each number in the table represents a measurement in one quadrat. Frequency is a measure of abundance. For this investigation you want to know which site, if any, has more lesser celandine. Just looking at the raw data it is difficult to tell whether there is a difference in abundance between the two sites. To try making sense of the data, a good first step is to put the measurements into numerical order (Table 4.2).

Table 4.2 The data in Table 4.1 arranged in numerical order.

	Frequency								
Site 1	14	16	19	20	22	22	27	28	31	
Site 2	13	17	17	17	21	23	26	27	29	30

Already you can see that the data from the two sites look similar. To summarise and describe the data for each site (or each data set) you need to know how variable it is and you need a single number that best describes the data. The statistic used to describe the variability of the data is the **range**. This is simply a statement of the lowest number and the highest number in the data set. For Site 1 the range is 14 to 31.

■ What is the range for Site 2?

☐ The range for Site 2 is 13 to 30.

The statistic used to describe the data set is the **median**. This is a type of average and it is simply the middle number in the data set. For Site 1, nine measurements were taken so, to find the middle number, simply count along the row of figures for site one until you reach the fifth. This is 22. Do the same for Site 2, except this time 10 measurements were taken. Since there is an even number of measurements this means that there are two middle numbers. These are 21 and 23. To calculate the median, take the average of these two numbers, i.e. 21 + 23 divided by 2 = 22.

You can now conclude that there is unlikely to be a statistically significant difference in the frequency of lesser celandine at the two sites since the medians are identical and the ranges are very similar (they overlap almost completely). So, using two very simple statistics, you have confirmed your hypothesis that there is little difference in the abundance of lesser celandine at the two sites and described your data.

Another good way to compare two sets of data is to look at the degree to which their ranges overlap. Figure 4.24 represents three possible situations – A, B and C – where the ranges show different degrees of overlap. The range of each data set is depicted as a horizontal line. Situation A shows two data sets where the ranges completely overlap, like the lesser celandine example, and it is relatively straightforward to assume, therefore, that there is no significant difference between these two sets of data. In situation B the ranges do not overlap at all, so it is fairly safe to assume that there is a significant difference between these two sets of data. What about the situation in C? Here there is considerable, but not total, overlap in the ranges. Does this mean there is a significant difference between these two sets of data or not?

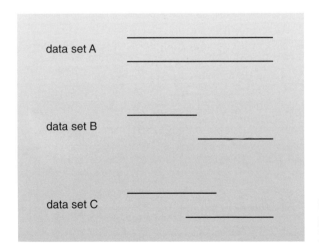

data set A

data set B

data set C

Figure 4.24   Three pairs of data sets – A, B and C. The horizontal lines represent the ranges.

This will be considered shortly but, before moving on, look at some more data to consolidate what has been covered so far (Table 4.3). Again, nine quadrats were used at Site 1 and ten quadrats were used at Site 2. Each number in the table represents a measurement taken in one quadrat.

Table 4.3 Frequency of bluebells (*Hyacinthoides non-scripta*) recorded at two sites in the same woodland.

	Frequency									
Site 1	10	12	14	14	15	17	24	25	26	
Site 2	27	27	30	32	33	35	40	46	52	57

■ Using the data in Table 4.3, calculate the range and the median for the frequency of bluebells. Is there likely to be a statistically significant difference in the frequency of bluebells at the two sites?

☐ The range for Site 1 is 10 to 26 and the median is 15. The range for Site 2 is 27 to 57 and the median is 34. (Note: in this case, an even number of quadrats was used so, to calculate the median, you need to take the average of the two middle numbers, i.e. $33 + 35 \div 2 = 34$.)

There is likely to be a statistically significant difference in the frequency of bluebells at the two sites since there is no overlap in the ranges. (This is similar to situation B in Figure 4.24) Since the median for Site 2 is greater than the median for Site 1, you can conclude that there are more bluebells at Site 2 than at Site 1.

Table 4.4 Frequency of wood anemone (*Anemone nemorosa*) recorded at two sites in the same woodland.

	Frequency								
Site 1	8	10	14	15	19	22	23	27	36
Site 2	4	6	7	9	10	12	13	15	21

Nine quadrats were used at both Site 1 and Site 2. Each number represents a measurement taken in one quadrat.

■ Using the data in Table 4.4, calculate the range and the median for the frequency of wood anemones. Is there likely to be a statistically significant difference in the frequency of wood anemones at the two sites?

☐ The range for Site 1 is 8 to 36 and the median is 19. The range for Site 2 is 4 to 21 and the median is 10.

The medians indicate that there may be more wood anemones at Site 1 but, since the ranges are overlapping, you cannot say whether the observed difference is statistically significant or whether it could have occurred by chance. (This is similar to situation C in Figure 4.24.) You will have to do a statistical test to find out.

Using a statistical test: the Mann–Whitney U Test

The test used here is the Mann–Whitney *U* Test. Like another statistical test – the *Z* test, which you will use in Activity D – it compares two sets of data. However, in Activity C the sets of data are smaller than those in Activity D and the data is unlikely to be normally distributed. This makes the Mann–Whitney *U* Test more suitable in this case. It is also easier to calculate!

This test works by comparing the medians of two sets of data. It does this by measuring the amount of overlap between the ranges of the two data sets. This section leads you through a worked example of the Mann–Whitney *U* Test and then you will have an opportunity to try out an example on your own.

Before doing the statistical test you must state the null hypothesis. This is important since it will help you interpret the results. The Mann–Whitney *U* Test assumes that any observed difference between two data sets has occurred by chance alone. This assumption is the null hypothesis. It tests this assumption and tells you whether it is valid or not. In the example in Table 4.4 the null hypothesis is: *there is no difference in the frequency of wood anemones at Site 1 and Site 2.*

The easiest way to calculate the Mann–Whitney *U* Test is to use a table such as Table 4.5.

Table 4.5 Example of a table for calculating the Mann–Whitney *U* Test, showing data for wood anemone arranged in numerical order, illustrating step 1.

Site	Raw data in numerical order	Rank	Rank for Site 1	Rank for Site 2
2	4			
2	6			
2	7			
1	8			
2	9			
1	10			
2	10			
2	12			
2	13			
1	14			
1	15			
2	15			
1	19			
2	21			
1	22			
1	23			
1	27			
1	36			
Sum of ranks				

Step 1

Put the raw data from both sites in numerical order from lowest to highest in the second column of the table. Put the site number in the first column (see Table 4.5).

Step 2

In the third column, assign a rank value for each raw data value starting with 1 for the lowest value. If any of the values are the same (tied values) then you calculate the average of the two ranks, e.g. in these data the sixth and seventh highest values are both 10. The average of the two available ranks is $6 + 7 \div 2 = 6.5$. Both values of 10 are assigned the rank of 6.5. The next highest value is 12. This is assigned the rank of 8 (Table 4.6).

Table 4.6 Ranks assigned in column 3, illustrating step 2.

Site	Raw data in numerical order	Rank	Rank for Site 1	Rank for Site 2
2	4	1		
2	6	2		
2	7	3		
1	8	4		
2	9	5		
1	10	6.5		
2	10	6.5		
2	12	8		
2	13	9		
1	14	10		
1	15	11.5		
2	15	11.5		
1	19	13		
2	21	14		
1	22	15		
1	23	16		
1	27	17		
1	36	18		
Sum of ranks				

Step 3

Write down all the ranks for Site 1 in the fourth column and those for Site 2 in the fifth column (Table 4.7).

Step 4

Calculate the sum of ranks for Site 1 by adding up all the figures in column 4. Write your answer in the box at the bottom of the column. Do the same for Site 2 (Table 4.7).

Table 4.7 Calculation of sum of ranks for steps 3 and 4.

Site	Raw data in numerical order	Rank	Rank for Site 1	Rank for Site 2
2	4	1		1
2	6	2		2
2	7	3		3
1	8	4	4	
2	9	5		5
1	10	6.5	6.5	
2	10	6.5		6.5
2	12	8		8
2	13	9		9
1	14	10	10	
1	15	11.5	11.5	
2	15	11.5		11.5
1	19	13	13	
2	21	14		14
1	22	15	15	
1	23	16	16	
1	27	17	17	
1	36	18	18	
Sum of ranks			111	60

Step 5

Now calculate the test statistics for each site (referred to as U_1 and U_2) using the formulae:

$$U_1 = (n_1 \times n_2) + ((n_2 \times (n_2 + 1)) \div 2) - \text{sum of ranks for Site 2}$$

$$U_2 = (n_1 \times n_2) + ((n_1 \times (n_1 + 1)) \div 2) - \text{sum of ranks for Site 1}$$

where n_1 is the number of measurements at Site 1 and n_2 is the number of measurements at Site 2.

Substituting the data into the formulae:

$$U_1 = (9 \times 9) + ((9 \times (9 + 1)) \div 2) - 60$$
$$= (9 \times 9) + ((9 \times 10) \div 2) - 60$$
$$= 81 + 45 - 60 = 66$$
$$U_2 = (9 \times 9) + ((9 \times (9 + 1)) \div 2) - 111$$
$$= (9 \times 9) + ((9 \times 10) \div 2) - 111$$
$$= 81 + 45 - 111 = 15$$

So, $U_1 = 66$ and $U_2 = 15$.

Step 6

Select the smallest U value ($U_2 = 15$). This is your final test statistic which you need to compare with the critical values in Appendix 3. Your sample sizes (n_1 and n_2) are both 9. Look along the row $n_2 = 9$ until you reach the column $n_1 = 9$. The critical value is 17. The paragraph at the top of the table in Appendix 3 tells you that the null hypothesis is rejected if U is less than or equal to the critical value. Since your calculated value of U is less than 17, you can reject the null hypothesis that *there is no difference in the frequency of wood anemones at Site 1 and Site 2*. Therefore, you can conclude that there is a statistically significant difference in the frequency of wood anemones at the two sites. Since the median value at Site 1 is greater than that at Site 2, you can also conclude that wood anemones are more frequent at Site 1.

Question 4.2

Try this example for yourself. It will give you some practice before you do it with your own data in Activity C.

On an experimental farm in East Anglia a study was carried out into the conservation value of different management methods of set-aside field margins around wheat fields. Two types of field margin were compared in this study. One was sown with a seed mixture containing wild flowers and grasses and the other was sown with a seed mixture containing grasses only. The experimenters suspected that the type of seed mixture used may affect the abundance of ground beetles (Coleoptera: Carabidae) in the margins. To investigate this, they laid nine pitfall traps (a device buried in the ground for capturing **invertebrates**) in each margin. The traps were left for one week and the numbers of beetles caught in each trap were counted.

The results are shown in Table 4.8.

Table 4.8 Number of ground beetles caught in pitfall traps in field margins sown with different seed mixtures.

Treatment	Number of beetles in each trap								
Wildflower and grass mix	29	10	14	17	5	8	20	7	26
Grass-only mix	9	6	2	3	11	2	15	0	8

■ What is the null hypothesis for this study?

☐ There is no significant difference in the number of ground beetles trapped in the wildflower margin and the grassy margin.

1 Calculate the median and the range for each treatment.

2 Use the Mann–Whitney U Test to compare both treatments. (Table 4.9 will help you do this).

When you have done this you should be able to answer the following questions.

(a) Is there a significant difference in the number of ground beetles in each treatment?

(b) On which type of field margin are ground beetles more abundant?

Table 4.9 Table for the Mann–Whitney U Test in Question 4.2.

Treatment	Raw data in numerical order	Rank	Rank for wildflower and grass mix	Rank for grass-only mix
Sum of ranks				

4.2.5 The Residential School

On the fieldwork day at your Residential School you will learn some relatively simple methods that are widely used by ecologists to quantify data in terrestrial habitats. Having studied this preparatory material, you should be in a good position to contribute to discussions about the factors that may be important in the locations you investigate and to reach conclusions about the data you collect in the field.

4.3 What to do next

You can check that you have understood the material in this chapter by working through the online interactive self-assessment questions for Chapter 4. You can access these questions via the link on the SXR103 course website.

You should now read Part I of the workbook for Activity C 'Investigating the environment', which describes the locations you will visit during the Residential School.

4.4   Summary of Chapter 4

The learning outcomes for Part I of Activity D are listed in the workbook.

Sections 4.1.1 and 4.1.2 summarise the biology that you are expected to know for Activity D before starting *Practising science*, whereas Section 4.1.3 is Part I of Activity D.

The ecology covered in Section 4.2 can be summarised as follows.

Ecology is the study of the interactions between organisms and their environment (including other organisms). Interactions can be biotic or abiotic. An understanding of ecology is important to inform environmental decision-making.

Soil pH influences the availability of mineral nutrients to plants and hence the distribution of different plant species. Some species can be classified as either calcicoles or calcifuges.

Variation in salinity, exposure to desiccation and biotic interactions (e.g. grazing) influence the zonation of seaweeds and animals on rocky shores.

Field studies usually involve collecting quantitative data in as objective a way as possible. Transects are often taken across field sites where an environmental gradient is suspected. Quadrats at various scales, including point quadrats, are used to estimate frequency or the proportion of area occupied by different plant species.

Now that you have completed Chapter 4 you should be able to:

- define ecology
- describe some biotic and abiotic interactions
- describe some of the ways in which soil pH influences the distribution of organisms
- describe some of the reasons why seaweeds and some animals display zonation on rocky shores
- describe in general terms how transects, quadrats and point quadrats can be used objectively to collect quantitative data about field sites
- understand when to use random sampling or transects
- understand why statistics are used in ecology
- calculate median and range and understand the principles of the Mann–Whitney *U* Test.

Chapter 5
Chemistry: analysis, reactions and structures

5.1   Introduction

Chemistry is about the structures of materials, their properties and reactions. The chemistry input at the Residential School is associated mainly with Activity B 'Analysing our environment'. The chemistry in this activity is concerned with how to analyse the environment. How do we know what pollutants are present? How do we know how much of the substance there is? What about an unknown substance? How do we unravel its structure? You will spend a lot of time with colourful reactions and spectra, yet carry out careful analysis at the part per million level! This preparatory material is not an introduction to chemistry from scratch. As you will see, we expect you to have some familiarity with *basic* chemical concepts already. Its aims are to reinforce these chemical concepts and the mathematical skills underpinning the laboratory work you will do in chemistry. At the same time, a few chemical concepts will be introduced that you may not have met before.

This preparatory material uses the workbook for Activity B to introduce the various chemical concepts described, so you will need to keep the workbook handy. You should try to answer the questions posed in the workbook, writing your answers in pencil in the spaces provided. You can discuss your answers with your tutor at the Residential School. Don't worry if you are unsure of any answers – they will be much more obvious when you carry out the experiments for yourself.

5.2   Activity B 'Analysing our environment'

Activity B introduces two important concepts: a chemical test for an unknown substance and calculating concentrations.

5.2.1 A chemical test for an unknown substance

Suppose you have a salt consisting of an unknown metal ion (positive) and an unknown negative ion, such as sulfate, chloride or carbonate. Chemists have created a series of chemical tests that will identify which metal ion is present. Similarly, another series of chemical tests has been developed for negative ions, so that the overall identity of the material may be discovered. In the first part of Activity B, we ask you to carry out a series of reactions on known metal ions and thus identify some key tests for particular metal ions. Then we give you an unknown sample, of the kind you might get in any analytical laboratory, and ask you to determine its identity.

Most of these tests involve precipitation reactions. Essentially, two soluble salts are mixed, for example, aqueous sodium chloride (containing Na^+ and Cl^- ions) and aqueous silver nitrate (containing Ag^+ and NO_3^- ions).

Whereas sodium chloride, silver nitrate and sodium nitrate are soluble in water, silver chloride is not and thus forms a white precipitate when the two solutions are mixed. Note that in the equation the state symbol (aq) indicates the soluble species and the state symbol (s) denotes the formation of a precipitate.

$$Na^+ + (aq) + Cl^-(aq) + Ag^+(aq) + NO_3^-(aq) \longrightarrow Na^+(aq) + NO_3^-(aq) + AgCl(s) \tag{5.19}$$

■ Rewrite Equation 5.19 without the ions that appear on both sides of the equation.

□ The spectator ions, as they are called, are $Na^+(aq)$ and $NO_3^-(aq)$; their removal from Equation 5.19 leaves

$$Cl^-(aq) + Ag^+(aq) \longrightarrow AgCl(s) \tag{5.20}$$

Some precipitated salts are coloured, which provides another clue to the identity of an unknown sample.

Read through Part A1 of the Activity B workbook to see how such reactions will be used to identify unknown metal ions. If you have time, try to complete Table A2 in Part A1, listing the positive and negative ions of the metal salts before you attend the Residential School, where your tutor will discuss the answers with you. You may find the Periodic Table in Appendix 4 useful.

Note that you are given the formula and charge of the nitrate ion so you can work out the charge on the positive ion(s) in the compound, because the number of negative charges on the negative ions must balance the number of positive charges on the metal ion. For example, chloride ion is Cl^-, and the chemical formula of magnesium chloride is $MgCl_2$. The formula indicates that one magnesium ion is associated with two chloride ions, so overall there are two negative charges ($2Cl^-$). This is balanced by the charge on the magnesium ion, which must therefore carry a 2+ charge (Mg^{2+}).

5.2.2 Calculating concentrations

In Part A2 of Activity B you will dilute a **standard solution** (of known concentration) of aluminium sulfate to give a range of solutions whose concentrations you will calculate on the basis of the dilution factors. These solutions will then be used to calibrate an instrument called a colorimeter, which you will use to measure the concentration of aluminium in an unknown water sample. You will then assess whether the aluminium concentration in this water sample is within the acceptable concentration limits set for drinking water. Remember, chemists usually talk about concentrations in terms of mol litre^{-1}. This is equivalent to the amount of the substance in moles contained in 1.0 litre of solution.

Suppose the standard solution is a 0.100 mol litre^{-1} solution of aluminium sulfate (in fact, it is much more dilute than this). This concentration is equivalent to that obtained by adding sufficient water to 0.100 **mole** of aluminium sulfate to make up one litre of solution.

■ What is the **molar mass** of aluminium sulfate, $Al_2(SO_4)_3$? (You will need to use the values for **relative atomic masses** given in Table A4.1 in Appendix 4.)

□ The relative molecular mass of $Al_2(SO_4)_3$ is $\{2Al (= 2 \times 27.0) + 3SO_4 (= 3 \times (32.1 + 4 \times 16.0)\} = 342.3$, therefore the molar mass is 342.3 g mol^{-1}.

■ How many grams of aluminium sulfate will one litre of 0.100 mol litre^{-1} aluminium sulfate contain?

☐ One litre of 0.100 mol litre^{-1} aluminium sulfate contains
0.100×342.3 g $= 34.2$ g of aluminium sulfate.

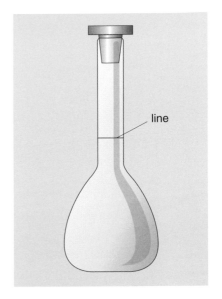

In preparing this solution you would have to weigh out the 34.2 g of aluminium sulfate and add water until the volume reaches a litre. This is why we refer to a litre of solution each time: you would not add a litre of water because 34.2 g of aluminium sulfate will itself occupy some of the volume. The precise volume – 1000 cm^3 – is achieved by using a special piece of glassware called a volumetric flask (Figure 5.2). The line is marked at 1000 cm^3.

line

■ Suppose you want to make only 250 cm^3 of the 0.1 mol litre^{-1} aluminium sulfate solution. How much aluminium sulfate would you put in a 250 cm^3 volumetric flask and make up to 250 cm^3 of solution?

☐ A volume of 250 cm^3 is 0.25 litre (250 cm$^3 \div 1000$ cm^3), so you need only use one-quarter of 34.2 g, which is 8.55 g.

Figure 5.1   A volumetric flask.

Now do the calculation the other way round, starting with the mass of the salt and working out its concentration.

■ A solution of aluminium sulfate is made by taking 1.0 g of aluminium sulfate (Al$_2$(SO$_4$)$_3$) and adding sufficient water to make 200 cm^3 of final solution. What is its concentration in mol litre^{-1}?

☐ The molar mass of aluminium sulfate is 342.3 g mol^{-1}. Thus 1.0 g of aluminium sulfate is equivalent to 1.0 g $\div$ 342.3 g mol$^{-1} = 2.9 \times 10^{-3}$ mol. This is contained in 200 cm^3. The amount that is contained in 1 cm^3 of this solution is 2.9×10^{-3} mol $\div$ 200 cm^3, and the amount that is therefore contained in one litre of this solution is $(2.9 \times 10^{-3}$ mol $\div$ 200 cm$^3) \times$ 1000 cm$^3 = 1.5 \times 10^{-2}$ mol. The concentration is therefore 1.5×10^{-2} mol litre^{-1}. Note that the final answer is given to the same number of significant figures (two in this case) as the initial amount of aluminium sulfate (1.0 g).

■ If you take 25 cm^3 of this solution and add sufficient water to make a final volume of 100 cm^3, what is the final concentration?

☐ The simplest way to do this type of calculation is to determine the factor by which the solution has been diluted. You begin with 25 cm^3 and end up with 100 cm^3, so the volume has increased by a factor of 100 $\div$ 25 $= 4$ and thus diluted the solution by a factor of 4. Therefore, the final concentration is 1.5×10^{-2} mol litre$^{-1} \div 4 = 3.8 \times 10^{-3}$ mol litre^{-1}.

Activity 5.1   Calculating dilutions and plotting graphs

Suggested study time: 40 minutes

In this activity you will practise the dilution calculations and graph plotting needed for Part A2 of Activity B. You will use the graph to estimate the aluminium concentration of an unknown water sample, given the absorbance, and thus decide whether the water is suitable for drinking, based on the acceptable levels.

(a) Read through Part A2 of the Activity B workbook. Using the hypothetical data in Table 5.1 below, calculate the concentration of aluminium in mol litre^{-1} for each solution (the concentration of the standard solution is 8.0×10^{-5} mol litre^{-1}).

(b) On the graph paper in Figure 5.2, plot a graph of absorbance against the concentration you calculated in Table 5.1, and draw the best-fit straight line through the origin.

(c) An unknown water sample has an absorbance of 0.75. From your graph, read off the concentration of aluminium in mol litre^{-1} in the unknown solution that corresponds to this absorbance and thus calculate the concentration of aluminium in ppm, as discussed in Task A4 of the Activity B workbook.

For the answers to this activity refer to the section at the end of this book.

Table 5.1 The dependence of absorbance on concentration.

Solution number	Number of 10 cm³ portions of standard solution	Concentration of aluminium/mol litre^{-1}	Absorbance
Distilled water	0		0
1	2		0.40
2	3		0.60
3	4		0.90
4	5		1.15

Figure 5.2 Graph paper for use with Activity 5.1.

5.3   What to do next

You can check that you have understood the material in this chapter by working through the online interactive self-assessment questions for Chapter 5. You can access these questions via the link on the SXR103 course website.

5.4   Summary of Chapter 5

Chemical reactions involving the formation of a precipitate can often be used to identify an unknown structure.

A mole of something contains 6×10^{23} 'somethings'. Thus, a mole of a substance contains 6×10^{23} particles (atoms or molecules) of that substance. A mole of an element has a mass equivalent to the relative atomic mass in grams. Similarly, a mole of a compound is equivalent to the sum of the relative atomic masses of the atoms in the formula unit (given by the chemical formula).

Concentrations are usually measured in mol litre^{-1}. This is equivalent to the amount of the substance in moles contained in 1.0 litre of solution.

Now that you have completed Chapter 5 you should be able to:

- interpret chemical equations as descriptions of reactions either at the atomic level (atoms, ions and/or molecules) or at the macro level (moles of reactants and products)
- identify metal ions in solution using simple reactions that form precipitates
- calculate the concentrations of solutions in mol litre^{-1} and parts per million from amounts expressed as grams of solute dissolved in a volume of solution expressed in cm^3.

Answers to activities

Activity 2.1

west   east

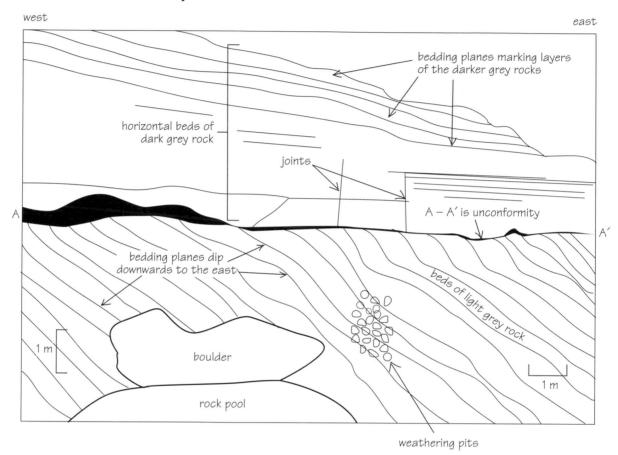

Figure 2.21   A sketch of the exposure shown in Figure 2.17a. The exposure is about 10 m high.

Activity 3.1

Task 1

(a)

(i) You know the wavelength, λ, since you are using a standard wavelength source.

(ii) The unknown quantity is d, the spacing of the grating.

(iii) The angle of diffraction, θ_n, is measured in the experiment. The order of diffraction, n, is also measured in the experiment (since you count the number of orders of diffraction from the straight through position).

(b) The two measured quantities are θ_n and n. Equation 3.4 does not describe a straight-line relationship between these two quantities because the equation is in terms of the *sine* of the angle of diffraction. The general equation of a straight-line graph passing through the origin is $y = kx$. Equation 3.4 is

$$\sin \theta_n = \frac{n\lambda}{d}$$

This can be rewritten to give:

$$\sin \theta_n = \left(\frac{\lambda}{d}\right) n$$

so there is a straight-line relationship between $\sin \theta_n$ and n. Therefore, by taking the sine of the angle of diffraction, you should get a straight-line relationship.

(c) If $\sin \theta_n$ is plotted against n you would expect the graph to be a straight line though the origin with a gradient of $(\lambda \div d)$. So you could find d by measuring the gradient of the graph, and using the known value of λ:

$$d = \frac{\lambda}{\text{gradient}}$$

Task 2

The values of $\sin \theta_n$ are shown in Table 3.6.

Task 3

(a) Figure 3.22 shows a graph of $\sin \theta_n$ against n.

Table 3.6 Completed version of Table 3.1.

n	$\theta_n/°$	$\sin \theta_n$
0	0.0	0.000
1	12.1	0.210
2	25.1	0.424
3	39.2	0.632
4	57.5	0.843

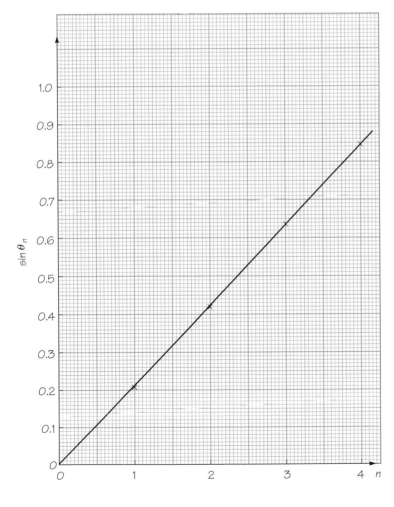

Figure 3.22 Graph of $\sin \theta_n$ against n (answer to Task 3a of Activity 3.1).

(b) The gradient is 'rise over run'. For the best-fit line shown here:

$$\text{gradient} = \frac{\text{rise}}{\text{run}} = \frac{0.741 - 0.109}{3.5 - 0.5} = \frac{0.632}{3} = 0.211$$

Note that there is no unit associated with this gradient because there is no unit associated with either $\sin \theta_n$ or n.

(c) The spacing of the grating is:

$$d = \frac{\lambda}{\text{gradient}}$$

so

$$d = \frac{632.8 \text{ nm}}{0.211} = 2999 \text{ nm} = 2999 \times 10^{-9} \text{ m} = 2.999 \times 10^{-6} \text{ m}$$

because 1 nm = 10^{-9} m.

The spacing of the grating is 3000 nm or 3.00×10^{-6} m, to 3 significant figures.

Activity 3.2

Task 1

The completed radioactive decay scheme for uranium-238 is shown in Table 3.7.

To show how you should have worked out the decay process at each stage, consider Step 5, the decay of $^{230}_{90}$Th to $^{226}_{88}$Ra. The mass number of $^{230}_{90}$Th is 230 and its atomic number is 90. The mass number of $^{226}_{88}$Ra is 226 (four less than the mass number of $^{230}_{90}$Th) and the atomic number of $^{226}_{88}$Ra is 88 (two less than the atomic number of $^{230}_{90}$Th). Thus, for the equation to balance, another decay product is needed with a mass number of four and a charge of two. The helium nucleus $^{4}_{2}$He meets these criteria, thus the decay is the α-decay:

$$^{230}_{90}\text{Th} \longrightarrow {}^{226}_{88}\text{Ra} + {}^{4}_{2}\text{He} + \text{energy}$$

Now consider step 9, the decay of $^{214}_{82}$Pb (a radioactive isotope of lead), to $^{214}_{83}$Bi. In this case, the mass number of the parent ($^{214}_{82}$Pb) and of the daughter ($^{214}_{83}$Bi) are both 214, whereas the atomic number of the daughter is one *more* than that of the parent. Thus, to balance the equation, another decay product is needed with a zero mass number and a charge of −1. The electron meets these criteria, thus the decay is the β⁻-decay:

$$^{214}_{82}\text{Pb} \longrightarrow {}^{214}_{83}\text{Bi} + e^- + \bar{\nu}_e + \text{energy}$$

The decay processes at the other stages can be found in a similar way.

Task 2

Taking a value for c, the speed of light, of 3.00×10^8 m^{-1} gives a corresponding energy of

$$E = mc^2 = 9.2 \times 10^{-29} \text{ kg} \times (3.00 \times 10^8 \text{ m s}^{-1})^2 = 8.3 \times 10^{-12} \text{ J}$$

Note that this is a very small amount of energy (compare it with the kinetic energy of a running child, which is about 1 J). However, this is only the energy corresponding to the decay of a single atom.

Table 3.7 Completed Table 3.2.

Step	Parent	Decay	Daughter
1	$^{238}_{92}$U	α	$^{234}_{90}$Th
2	$^{234}_{90}$Th	β⁻	$^{234}_{91}$Pa
3	$^{234}_{91}$Pa	β⁻	$^{234}_{92}$U
4	$^{234}_{92}$U	α	$^{230}_{90}$Th
5	$^{230}_{90}$Th	α	$^{226}_{88}$Ra
6	$^{226}_{88}$Ra	α	$^{222}_{86}$Rn
7	$^{222}_{86}$Rn	α	$^{218}_{84}$Po
8	$^{218}_{84}$Po	α	$^{214}_{82}$Pb
9	$^{214}_{82}$Pb	β⁻	$^{214}_{83}$Bi
10	$^{214}_{83}$Bi	β⁻	$^{214}_{84}$Po
11	$^{214}_{84}$Po	α	$^{210}_{82}$Pb
12	$^{210}_{82}$Pb	β⁻	$^{210}_{83}$Bi
13	$^{210}_{83}$Bi	β⁻	$^{210}_{84}$Po
14	$^{210}_{84}$Po	α	$^{206}_{82}$Pb (stable)

Activity 3.3

Tasks 1 and 2

The completed graph is shown in Figure 3.23.

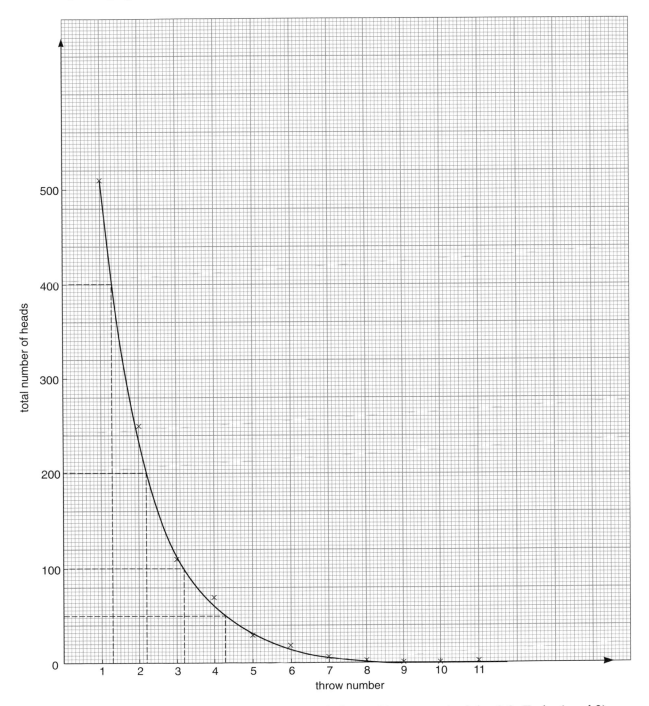

Figure 3.23   Total number of heads thrown at each throw. (Answer to Activity 3.3, Tasks 1 and 2).

Task 3

(a) The half-life found by considering the interval between 400 heads thrown and 200 heads thrown is 2.2 − 1.3 throws = 0.9 of a throw.

The half-life found by considering the interval between 200 heads thrown and 100 heads thrown is 3.2 − 2.2 throws = 1.0 throws.

The half-life found by considering the interval between 100 heads thrown and 50 heads thrown is 4.3 − 3.2 throws = 1.1 throws.

The mean is 1.0 throws.

(b) This is probably the value you expected; on average, for each throw half of the coins will be heads and thus be discarded.

(c) A graph for a very large set of data would have the same general shape, and the half-life would also be the same (to within experimental uncertainty). However, the actual number of heads thrown on each throw would be much greater and the data would be a closer fit to a smooth curve.

(d) The graphs have the same general shape (known as a falling exponential) which is a characteristic of any process of this kind.

Careful inspection of the axes indicates that fewer sixes than heads are thrown per throw and it takes considerably more throws for all the dice to be put to one side. This is reasonable, given that there are six possible outcomes every time a dice is thrown, but just two when a coin is tossed.

The mean half-life for the data given in Figure 3.15 is about 3.9 throws. This value is entirely consistent with the detailed theory of this simulation (which is beyond the scope of this course). The important point is that it is a longer time interval than the equivalent value for coins. Again this is what you would expect − dice take longer to 'decay' than coins, which is reflected in a longer half-life.

Activity 5.1

(a) First you need to calculate the concentrations obtained after diluting the standard solution. As already discussed, the simplest way to do this type of calculation is to determine the factor the solution has been diluted by. In solution 1 you begin with 20 cm^3 (2 × 10 cm^3) and end up with 100 cm^3 so the volume has increased by a factor of 100 ÷ 20 = 5 and thus diluted the solution by a factor of 5. Thus the final concentration is 8.0×10^{-5} mol litre^{-1} ÷ 5 = 1.6×10^{-5} mol litre^{-1}.

While this method of calculation works well for volumes that divide easily into 100 cm^3, what about volumes such as 30 cm^3? Well, the strategy is similar. You begin with 30 cm^3 and end up with 100 cm^3 so the volume has increased by a factor of 100 ÷ 30 = 3.33 and thus diluted the solution by a factor of 3.33. Therefore, the final concentration is 8.0×10^{-5} mol litre^{-1} ÷ 3.33 = 2.4×10^{-5} mol litre^{-1}.

Following a similar strategy for the rest of the data in Table 5.1 gives Table 5.2.

Table 5.2 The dependence of absorbance on concentration.

Solution number	Number of 10 cm³ portions of standard solution	Concentration of aluminium/mol litre⁻¹	Absorbance
Distilled water	0	0	0
1	2	1.6×10^{-5}	0.40
2	3	2.4×10^{-5}	0.60
3	4	3.2×10^{-5}	0.90
4	5	4.0×10^{-5}	1.15

(b) The next task is to plot the graph of absorbance *against* concentration. This means that the absorbance – the quantity that you would measure – is the y-axis (vertical axis) and the concentration is the x-axis (horizontal axis). The absorbance varies from 0 to 1.15 so, because there are 13 major divisions up the page, it is most convenient to make one major division equal to 0.1 absorbance units. Similarly, there are nine major divisions across the page so one major division equals 0.5×10^{-5} mol litre⁻¹. Plotting the data in Table 5.2 gives the graph in Figure 5.3. Note: if you plotted the absorbance on the x-axis (horizontal axis) and the concentration on the y-axis (vertical axis) you should still have been able to measure

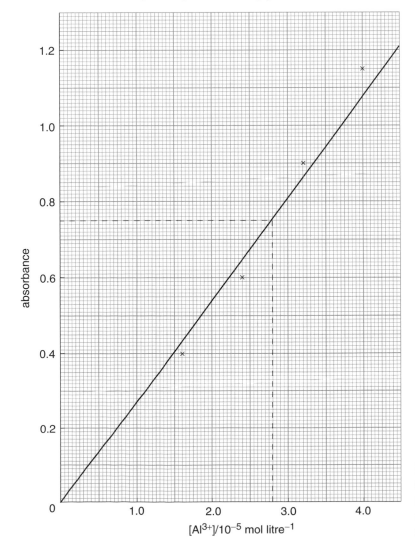

Figure 5.3 Plot of absorbance against concentration of aluminium.

109

the correct unknown concentration from the graph. However, if you had been asked to calculate the gradient, m, your value would be $1 \div m$.

The graph shows that the points all lie in a straight line, within experimental error, thus justifying our request for you to draw a straight line. The line is forced through the origin because, if there is no aluminium present, the absorbance (arising from the aluminium) must be zero. The straight line confirms that the absorbance is *directly* proportional to the concentration, that is:

$$A = b[Al^{3+}]$$

where b is a constant and the gradient of your graph.

(c) The next step is to find the concentration of aluminium in an unknown water sample with an absorbance of 0.75. Figure 5.3 shows that the point on the line where the absorbance is 0.75 has a concentration of 2.8×10^{-5} mol litre^{-1}. Depending on where you draw your line, this value could be anything between 2.7 and 2.9×10^{-5} mol litre^{-1}.

The final stage is to convert the concentration of aluminium from mol litre^{-1} into ppm. A concentration of 2.8×10^{-5} mol litre^{-1} tells you that there is 2.8×10^{-5} mol of aluminium in 1 litre of water. The relative atomic mass of aluminium is 27.0 thus 1 litre contains $27.0 \times 2.8 \times 10^{-5} = 7.6 \times 10^{-4}$ g of aluminium (anything between 7.3 and 7.9×10^{-4} g is acceptable). Task A4 of the Activity B workbook tell you to assume that 1 litre has a mass of 1000 g. Thus 7.6×10^{-4} g of aluminium is contained in 1000 g. Put another way, 7.6×10^{-1} g of aluminium is contained in 1 000 000 g, which corresponds to 0.76 ppm (0.73–0.79 ppm).

■ Look at the maximum acceptable concentrations of metals in drinking water in Table 1 of the Activity B workbook. Is the unknown water sample safe to drink?

☐ The value you determined is greater than the maximum acceptable concentration of aluminium (0.2 ppm.) and so the sample is not fit to drink.

You are now ready to start the laboratory activities associated with this topic.

Answers to questions

Answers to questions

Question 2.1

Magma, such as volcanic lavas, which erupt at the Earth's surface will cool quickly so the crystals that form will be small, forming a fine-grained igneous rock.

On the other hand, magmas which are intruded deep in the Earth's crust will cool slowly giving large crystals time to form.

Question 2.2

Statement (c) is false and all the others are true. Grain size is irrelevant here, so can be ignored. Statement (c) does not indicate whether just mafic, intermediate or felsic rocks are being considered, so you need to consider all rocks. The size of the field for alkali feldspar (coloured pink) is smaller than the size of the field for plagioclase feldspar (coloured pale mauve), so there is less alkali feldspar than plagioclase feldspar. (Note that because you are comparing these two volumes qualitatively it does not matter that there is no numerical scale on the horizontal axis.)

Question 2.3

(a) (i) High because a large amount of energy is needed to transport the pebbles and boulders to the place where they are deposited.

(b) (iii) Low because very little energy is needed to move fine clay particles to the place where they are deposited.

(c) (ii) Medium because sand grains are medium sized. Larger sized grains of sediment cannot be transported to the place of deposition. Finer sediment will remain in transit and will not be deposited.

Question 2.4

(a) Rocks formed by regional metamorphism show foliation because of the alignment of platy minerals that grew during compression. Rocks formed by contact metamorphism do not show foliation.

(b) Contact metamorphic rocks are confined to a narrow band in the rocks surrounding an igneous intrusion. Regional metamorphism occurs in vast tracts of land as a result of mountain building.

Question 3.1

The typical size of a nucleus and an atom are 10^{-14} m and 10^{-10} m, respectively. So:

$$\frac{\text{diameter of nucleus}}{\text{diameter of atom}} = \frac{10^{-14} \text{ m}}{10^{-10} \text{ m}}$$

Both diameters are measured in metres, so the units cancel out:

$$\frac{\text{diameter of nucleus}}{\text{diameter of atom}} = \frac{10^{-14}}{10^{-10}}$$

This fraction can be simplified, because $10^{-14} \div 10^{-10} = 10^{-4}$.

The question asks for the answer to be expressed as $1 \div$ (a number), which is found using the fact that $10^{-n} = 1 \div 10^n$, so $10^{-4} = 1 \div 10^4$, which can be expressed as:

$$\frac{\text{diameter of nucleus}}{\text{diameter of atom}} = \frac{1}{10^4} = \frac{1}{10\,000}$$

Question 3.2

You should start by rearranging the diffraction equation (Equation 3.4) to make λ the subject:

$$\lambda = \frac{d \sin \theta_n}{n}$$

In this case, only the first order of diffraction is of interest, hence $n = 1$:

$$\lambda = d \sin \theta_n$$

The wavelengths can be found using this equation.

The wavelength of light that produces first order diffraction at $19.8°$ is:

$$\lambda = 1.669 \times 10^{-6}\,\text{m} \times \sin 19.8°$$
$$= 1.669 \times 10^{-6}\,\text{m} \times 0.339$$
$$= 5.65 \times 10^{-7}\,\text{m to 3 significant figures.}$$

The wavelength of light that produces first order diffraction at $23.4°$ is:

$$\lambda = 1.667 \times 10^{-6}\,\text{m} \times \sin 23.4°$$
$$= 1.667 \times 10^{-6}\,\text{m} \times 0.397$$
$$= 6.62 \times 10^{-7}\,\text{m to 3 significant figures.}$$

Question 3.3

$$\frac{\text{dose equivalent from atomic bombs}}{\text{dose equivalent from 'Rocks and radioactivity'}}$$

$$= \frac{5\,\text{Sv}}{1\,\mu\text{Sv}} = \frac{5\,\text{Sv}}{1 \times 10^{-6}\,\text{Sv}} = 5 \times 10^6 = 5\,000\,000 \text{ times greater.}$$

Question 3.4

$$\frac{m_\text{p}}{m_\text{e}} = \frac{1.673 \times 10^{-27}\,\text{kg}}{9.11 \times 10^{-31}\,\text{kg}} = 1840 \text{ to 3 significant figures.}$$

$$\text{So } m_\text{e} = \frac{1}{1840}\,m_\text{p}$$

Question 3.5

(a) The electrons in the atom can only have specific values of energy (i.e. specific energy levels). When substance X is heated, the electrons gain energy so are excited to higher energy levels. At these higher energy levels, the electrons are less stable than at lower energy levels, so the electrons immediately tend to lose energy and fall back to lower levels. They give up the excess energy in the form of photons of electromagnetic radiation, which are detected as spectral lines. The photon energy corresponding to each spectral line is the same as the *difference* in energy between the two energy levels involved in the transition. Photon energy and wavelength are related by the equation

$$E_{ph} = \frac{hc}{\lambda}$$

so each different transition between energy levels gives rise to a characteristic wavelength. (See Section 3.3.)

(b) $E_{ph} = (E_3 - E_2) = 3.03 \times 10^{-19}$ J and $E_{ph} = \frac{hc}{\lambda}$ (Equation 3.2).

Rearranging the latter gives:

$$\lambda = \frac{hc}{E_{ph}}$$

so

$$\lambda = \frac{6.63 \times 10^{-34} \text{ J s} \times 3.00 \times 10^8 \text{ m s}^{-1}}{3.03 \times 10^{-19} \text{ J}} = 6.56 \times 10^{-7} \text{ m to 3 significant figures.}$$

Converting this into nanometres gives $\lambda = 656$ nm.

Question 3.6

If $\sin \theta_n = \frac{n\lambda}{d}$ (Equation 3.4), rearranging it gives:

$$d = \frac{n\lambda}{\sin \theta_n}$$

so

$$d = \frac{1 \times 633 \times 10^{-9} \text{ m}}{\sin (30.4°)} = 1.25 \times 10^{-6} \text{ m} \text{ to 3 significant figures.}$$

Question 3.7

The acceleration is given by the gradient of the graph in Figure 3.24:

$$\text{gradient} = \frac{\text{rise}}{\text{run}} = \frac{(30 - 5) \text{ m s}^{-1}}{(3.0 - 0.5) \text{ s}} = \frac{25 \text{ m s}^{-1}}{2.5 \text{ s}} = 10 \text{ m s}^{-2}$$

Thus the stone's average acceleration is 10 m s^{-2}.

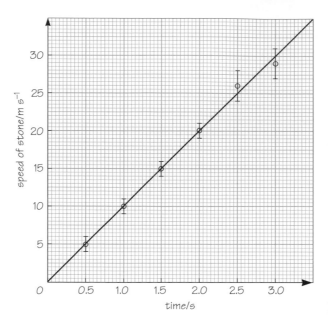

Figure 3.24 Completed plot of the data in Table 3.4.

Question 3.8

Radioactive decay is a random process, and a radioactive count of value n has an associated uncertainty of $\sqrt{n}$ (see Section 3.5.7). The uncertainties in Table 3.8 are rounded to the nearest whole number above (i.e. the whole number *greater* than the calculated value).

Table 3.8 Completed Table 3.5.

Elapsed time/min	Counts per minute	Uncertainty in the count rate per minute
1	403	21
2	320	18
3	249	16
4	201	15
5	157	13
6	128	12
7	109	11
8	89	10
9	71	9
10	66	9

Question 3.9

The half-life found by considering the time taken for the percentage of ^{14}C remaining to fall from 100% to 50% is $(5.8 - 0) \times 1000$ years = 5800 years.

The half-life found by considering the time taken for the percentage of ^{14}C remaining to fall from 80% to 40% is $(7.8 - 1.8) \times 1000$ years = 6000 years.

The half-life found by considering the time taken for the percentage of ^{14}C remaining to fall from 60% to 30% is $(10.2 - 4.3) \times 1000$ years = 5900 years.

The mean of these three values (i.e. the mean half-life) is $\dfrac{5800 + 6000 + 5900}{3}$ years = 5900 years. (See Section 3.5.5.)

Question 4.1

Random sampling is more appropriate for the investigation of the effects of salmonberry on the abundance of bluebells since the hypothesis is testing for a difference between two sites.

A transect is more appropriate for the investigation of the effects of flooding from the stream since the hypothesis is testing for a correlation between the abundance of bluebells and the percentage moisture content of the soil. There is a gradual change in the percentage moisture content of the soil along the transect.

Question 4.2

To calculate the median and the range, arrange the data in numerical order.

Wild flower	5	7	8	10	14	17	20	26	29
Grass-only	0	2	2	3	6	8	9	11	15

The median for the wildflower mix (WF) is 14 and the range is 5 to 29.

The median for the grass-only mix (G) is 6 and the range is 0 to 15.

Table 4.10 Completed Table 4.9.

Treatment	Raw data in numerical order	Rank	Rank for wildflower and grass mix	Rank for grass-only mix
G	0	1		1
G	2	2.5		2.5
G	2	2.5		2.5
G	3	4		4
WF	5	5	5	
G	6	6		6
WF	7	7	7	
WF	8	8.5	8.5	
G	8	8.5		8.5
G	9	10		10
WF	10	11	11	
G	11	12		12
WF	14	13	13	
G	15	14		14
WF	17	15	15	
WF	20	16	16	
WF	26	17	17	
WF	29	18	18	
Sum of ranks			110.5	60.5

Substituting into the formulae for U_1 and U_2:

$$U_1 = (9 \times 9) + ((9 \times 10) \div 2) - 60.5 = 81 + 45 - 60.5 = 65.5$$

$$U_2 = (9 \times 9) + ((9 \times 10) \div 2) - 110.5 = 81 + 45 - 110.5 = 15.5$$

The smaller U value is 15.5. The sample sizes (n_1 and n_2) are both 9. The critical value is 17. Since your calculated value of U is less than 17, you can reject the null hypothesis that *there is no difference in the number of ground beetles trapped in the wildflower margin and the grassy margin.* Therefore, you can conclude that there is a statistically significant difference in the number of ground beetles in the two types of field margin. Since the median value for the wildflower margin is greater than that for the grassy margin, you can also conclude that more ground beetles were trapped in the wildflower margin.

Appendix I Sines, cosines and tangents

Look at the triangle drawn in Figure A1.1a. One angle of this triangle is a right angle and is therefore equal to 90°. The side of the triangle facing this is the longest of the three sides and is called the **hypotenuse**. For convenience, it is labelled *hyp* in the diagram. Another of the angles of the triangle is labelled *θ*. The side of the triangle that is opposite the angle *θ* is labelled accordingly as *opp*, and the side adjacent to the angle is labelled *adj*.

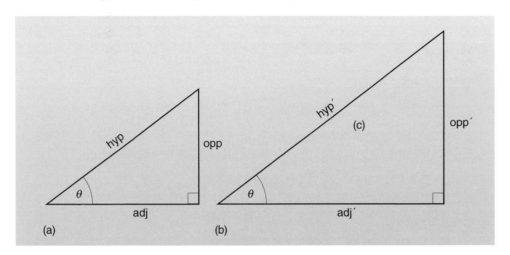

Figure A1.1   Two triangles of different sizes, but with the same angles as each other.

Question A1.1

Each of the angles of the triangle shown in Figure A1.1a is the same as the corresponding angle of the triangle in Figure A1.1b. Measure the lengths of the sides of these triangles (hyp, opp, adj in Figure A1.1a and hyp', opp', adj' in Figure A1.1b). What are the values of

$$\left(\frac{\text{opp}}{\text{hyp}}\right), \left(\frac{\text{adj}}{\text{hyp}}\right) \text{ and } \left(\frac{\text{opp}}{\text{adj}}\right)$$

for the triangle in Figure A1.1a? How do these compare with the values

$$\left(\frac{\text{opp'}}{\text{hyp'}}\right), \left(\frac{\text{adj'}}{\text{hyp'}}\right) \text{ and } \left(\frac{\text{opp'}}{\text{adj'}}\right)$$

for the triangle in Figure A1.1b?

As you saw in Question A1.1, the relative lengths of the sides of a right-angled triangle depend on the angles in that triangle. Turning this argument around, the sizes of the angles in a right-angled triangle depend on the relative lengths of the sides of these triangles. This is such a useful fact that the values you calculated above are given special names: **sine**, cosine and tangent, often abbreviated to sin, cos and tan. For the angle *θ* shown in Figure A1.1:

$$\sin\theta = \left(\frac{\text{opp}}{\text{hyp}}\right), \cos\theta = \left(\frac{\text{adj}}{\text{hyp}}\right) \text{ and } \tan\theta = \left(\frac{\text{opp}}{\text{adj}}\right)$$

These three trigonometric functions, as they are known, are stored on your calculator. So, for instance, if you key into your calculator: 3 0 SIN or SIN 3 0, depending on the operation of the calculator, it will display a value of 0.5. Therefore, the sine of 30° is 0.5. In any right-angled triangle, in which the length of one side divided by the length of the hypotenuse is 0.5, the angle opposite to the side in question is 30°. Sine, cosine and tangent functions refer to relative lengths of the sides of a right-angled triangle, and so are independent of the actual size of the triangle in question, as you saw in Question A1.1, and they have no units.

Answer to Question A1.1

The lengths of the side in the triangles shown are opp = 3.0 cm, adj = 4.0 cm, hyp = 5.0 cm, opp′ = 4.5 cm, adj′ = 6.0 cm and hyp′ = 7.5 cm. The values calculated for the smaller triangle are:

$$\frac{\text{opp}}{\text{hyp}} = \frac{3.0}{5.0} = 0.6 \,, \quad \frac{\text{adj}}{\text{hyp}} = \frac{4.0}{5.0} = 0.8 \ \text{and} \ \frac{\text{opp}}{\text{adj}} = \frac{3.0}{4.0} = 0.75$$

The values for the larger triangle are:

$$\left(\frac{\text{opp}'}{\text{hyp}'}\right) = \frac{4.5}{7.5} = 0.6 \,, \quad \left(\frac{\text{adj}'}{\text{hyp}'}\right) = \frac{6.0}{7.5} = 0.8 \ \text{and} \ \left(\frac{\text{opp}'}{\text{adj}'}\right) = \frac{4.5}{6.0} = 0.75 \,.$$

The relative lengths of the sides are therefore the same in triangles whose angles are the same.

In fact, the relative lengths of the sides of a triangle are the same for *any* triangle that has the same angles, however large or small the triangle is. But if you change the shape of the triangle, so that the angles are different, the relative lengths of the sides of the triangle are different too.

Appendix 2 The equation for a straight line

Imagine you are walking along a road at a constant speed. The distance travelled from your starting point will be proportional to the time taken, so in twice the time you will travel twice the distance. If you plot a graph of distance travelled against time taken, you would get a straight line passing through the origin of the graph. In fact, if values for the two quantities on either side of *any* proportionality relationship (such as $y \propto x$, i.e. $y = kx$, where k is a constant) are plotted against each other on a graph, the points will lie along a straight line that passes through the origin (Figure A2.1). The constant k is equal to the gradient of the graph, and can be calculated. Any equation that can be written in the form

$$y = kx$$

(often given as $y = mx$) is called 'an equation of a straight line'.

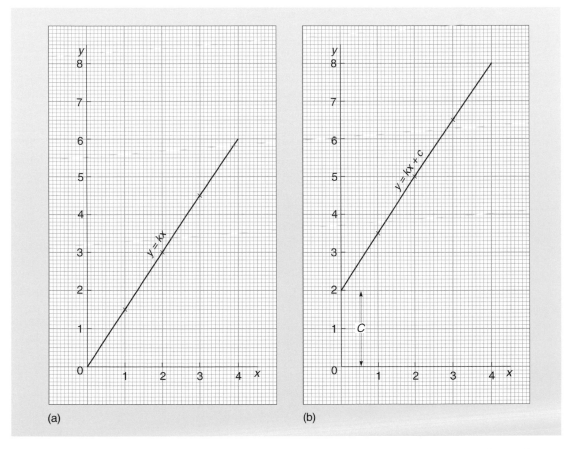

(a)   (b)

Figure A2.1   (a) Graph showing values of a quantity y plotted against corresponding values of x and illustrating the proportionality $y \propto x$. The gradient of this graph is k, such that $y = kx$. (b) Graph showing values of a quantity y plotted against x and illustrating the equation $y = kx + c$. The gradient of this graph is k and it intercepts the vertical axis at $y = c$.

Now look at the line plotted on the graph in Figure A2.1b. This has the same gradient as the graph in Figure A2.1a, but the whole line has been moved vertically upwards by a distance c. So, for any value of x, you can find the value of y by calculating kx as in Figure A2.1a, and then adding on an extra amount c, corresponding to the vertical shift. So the equation that allows you to calculate a value for y from a value of x is:

$$y = kx + c$$

This is the general form of the **equation of a straight line**. It is often given in a slightly different form, as $y = mx + c$, where m is the gradient.

From this equation you can see that, when $x = 0$, then $y = (k \times 0) + c$ and, therefore, $y = c$. So the value of c indicates the point at which the line intercepts the vertical axis. Such a graph still has a gradient of k (or m), however, as you can see by comparing the gradients of the two graphs in Figure A2.1. Figure A2.2 shows how a given straight-line graph relates to its equation.

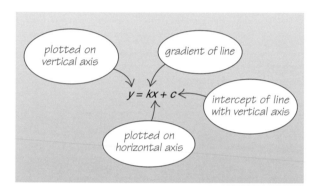

Figure A2.2   The equation of a straight line.

■   If c is a negative number, how would the graph differ from Figure A2.1b?

☐   The graph will still be a straight line and slope in the same direction, but it will shift downwards so that it intercepts the vertical axis in the region where y is negative.

Appendix 3 Statistical table for the Mann–Whitney *U* Test

Critical values of U at the 5% level. Reject your null hypothesis at the 5% level if your value of U is less than or equal to the tabulated value; n_1 and n_2 are the sample sizes.

$n_1 =$	1	2	3	4	5	6	7	8	9	10	11	12	13	14	15	16	17	18	19	20
$n_2 = 1$	–	–	–	–	–	–	–	–	–	–	–	–	–	–	–	–	–	–	–	–
$n_2 = 2$	–	–	–	–	–	–	–	0	0	0	0	1	1	1	1	1	2	2	2	2
$n_2 = 3$	–	–	–	–	0	1	1	2	2	3	3	4	4	5	5	6	6	7	7	8
$n_2 = 4$	–	–	–	0	1	2	3	4	4	5	6	7	8	9	10	11	11	12	13	13
$n_2 = 5$	–	–	0	1	2	3	5	6	7	8	9	11	12	13	14	15	17	18	19	20
$n_2 = 6$	–	–	1	2	3	5	6	8	10	11	13	14	16	17	19	21	22	24	25	27
$n_2 = 7$	–	–	1	3	5	6	8	10	12	14	16	18	20	22	24	26	28	30	32	34
$n_2 = 8$	–	0	2	4	6	8	10	13	15	17	19	22	24	26	29	31	34	36	38	41
$n_2 = 9$	–	0	2	4	7	10	12	15	17	20	23	26	28	31	34	37	39	42	45	48
$n_2 = 10$	–	0	3	5	8	11	14	17	20	23	26	29	33	36	39	42	45	48	52	55
$n_2 = 11$	–	0	3	6	9	13	16	19	23	26	30	33	37	40	44	47	51	55	58	62
$n_2 = 12$	–	1	4	7	11	14	18	22	26	29	33	37	41	45	49	53	57	61	65	69
$n_2 = 13$	–	1	4	8	12	16	20	24	28	33	37	41	45	50	54	59	63	67	72	76
$n_2 = 14$	–	1	5	9	13	17	22	26	31	36	40	45	50	55	59	64	67	74	78	83
$n_2 = 15$	–	1	5	10	14	19	24	29	34	39	44	49	54	59	64	70	75	80	85	90
$n_2 = 16$	–	1	6	11	15	21	26	31	37	42	47	53	59	64	70	75	81	86	92	98
$n_2 = 17$	–	2	6	11	17	22	28	34	39	45	51	57	63	67	75	81	87	93	99	105
$n_2 = 18$	–	2	7	12	18	24	30	36	42	48	55	61	67	74	80	86	93	99	106	112
$n_2 = 19$	–	2	7	13	19	25	32	38	45	52	58	65	72	78	85	92	99	106	113	119
$n_2 = 20$	–	2	8	13	20	27	34	41	48	55	62	69	76	83	90	98	105	112	119	127

Appendix 4 The Periodic Table

Figure A4.1 shows the complete Periodic Table for all the known chemical elements, The named blocks of elements have their own distinctive properties.

Table A4.1 Some relative atomic masses.

Element (symbol)	Relative atomic mass
hydrogen (H)	1.01
oxygen (O)	16.0
aluminium (Al)	27.0
sulfur (S)	32.1
chlorine (Cl)	35.5
copper (Cu)	63.5
zinc (Zn)	65.4

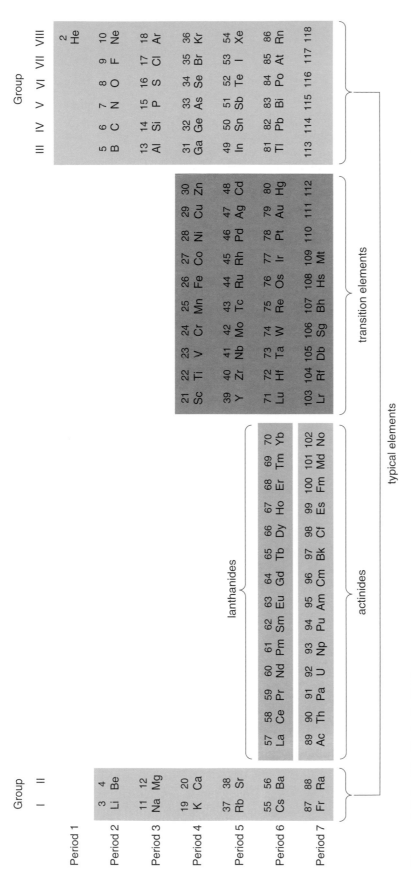

Figure A4.1   The Periodic Table.

Acknowledgements

Grateful acknowledgement is made to the following sources for permission to reproduce material in this book.

Figures

Cover: Andrew Pini;

Figure 2.1: IPR/15-22, Reproduced by permission of the British Geological Survey © NERC, All rights Reserved;

Figures 2.10 and 2.17: Peter Sheldon;

Figures 2.12, 3.19, 4.12b and 4.12c: Linda Fowler;

Figures 2.13a and c: British Mesozoic Fossils, 4th edn, © Trustees of the British Museum (Natural History) 1972;

Figure 2.13b: British Palaeozoic Fossils, 3rd edn, © Trustees of the British Museum (Natural History) 1969;

Figure 3.1: Reproduced by permission of JBM Almaden Research Centre;

Figure 3.7: Photographer Connor Lee, Wikipedia.com. Permission is granted under the terms of the GNU Free Documentation License;

Figures 4.8 and 4.15: Matt Compton;

Figures 4.12a, 4.18, 4.19 and 4.21: Donal O'Donnell;

Figure 4.13: Mike Dodd/Open University.

Every effort has been made to contact copyright holders. If any have been inadvertently overlooked the publishers will be pleased to make the necessary arrangements at the first opportunity.

SXR 103 Course Team

Original Academic contributors:

Evelyn Brown

Roger Beck

Mary Bell

Steve Blake

Bob Hill

Mark Jones

Sally Jordan

Jean McCloughry

Pat Murphy

Valda Stevens

Peter Taylor

Ruth Williams

Academic contributors for fourth edition:

Linda Fowler

Peter Morrod

Donal O'Donnell

Paul Hatherly

Jane Banks

Index

Entries and page numbers in **bold type** refer to terms defined in the online *Glossary*. Where the page number is given in *italics*, the indexed information is given mainly, or wholly, in a figure or table.